DECOMPOSITIONS OF OPERATOR ALGEBRAS. I

By

I. E. Segal

of the

University of Chicago

1. <u>Introduction</u>. We show that an algebra of operators on a
Hilbert space can be decomposed relative to a Boolean algebra of invariant
subspaces as a kind of direct integral, similar to the decomposition as a
direct sum of algebras of linear transformations on finite-dimensional
spaces. This decomposition results from an interesting decomposition
formula, for the "states" of operator algebras which we have treated in
[8]. If the Boolean algebra is maximal, and with a certain separability
restriction, the constituents in the direct integral are almost everywhere
irreducible. It follows that in the case of a separable Hilbert space, a
weakly closed self-adjoint algebra is a direct integral of factors. Any
continuous unitary representation of a separable locally compact group G
is a direct integral of irreducible such representations. If G is unimodular, then its two-sided regular representation is a direct integral of
irreducible two-sided representations. Any measure on a compact metric
space which is invariant under a group of homeomorphisms of the space is a
direct integral of ergodic measures.

Our basic results are closely related to results of von Neumann in
[16]. The decompositions obtained by von Neumann are from a formal view-

---

Received by the Editors on March 1, 1950.

I. E. Segal

point nearly identical with ours, but there are important technical differences in the approaches as well as in the results which allow us to give considerably simpler proofs of the key theorems, and which yield a theory better adapted to the study of group representations than that of von Neumann. These differences are notably, first, the use of states, and second, the use of perfect measure spaces, rather than a measure space over the field of Borel subsets of the reals. Each of these features simplifies the serious measurability problems involved in obtaining decompositions. The concept of direct integral of Hilbert spaces is awkward because the Hilbert spaces may vary in dimensionality, and it is unclear to begin with how a measurable function to such Hilbert spaces should be defined. As a state is a numerical-valued function, there is no such awkwardness about direct integrals of states, and by virtue of the known correspondence between states and representation Hilbert spaces, a decomposition of a state as such an integral induces a decomposition of the Hilbert space into "differential" Hilbert spaces, so to speak. The utilization of perfect measure spaces (on which every bounded measurable function is equivalent to a continuous function) eliminates the need for various kinds of sets of measure zero which occur in von Neumann's theory, and greatly facilitates the reduction of group representations. Our theorem concerning maximal decompositions bears the same formal relation to a theorem of Mautner [5] that our decomposition theory does to that of von Neumann, but the logical roles of these two theorems are very different, as we use our result to decompose a general algebra of operators into factors, while Mautner's result is derived directly from von Neumann's decomposition theory for general operator algebras. By virtue of the difference between our basic techniques (some of which apply to inseparable spaces) and those of von Neumann, our proofs are for the most part necessarily of a different character from those of von Neumann, and in particular no use is made of the theory of analytic sets.

2. <u>Definitions</u> <u>and</u> <u>notations</u>. We introduce here a number of
terms and symbols which we shall use without further reference in the remainder of the paper.

<u>Definition 2.1</u>. A <u>W*-algebra</u> (or <u>C*-algebra</u>) is a weakly (or uni-
formly) closed self-adjoint (SA) algebra of (bounded linear) operators on a
Hilbert space. The term "operator" will always mean "bounded linear operator". For any algebra $\mathcal{Q}$ of operators on a Hilbert space, the set of all
operators which commute with every element of $\mathcal{Q}$ is called the <u>commutor</u>
of $\mathcal{Q}$ and denoted by $\mathcal{Q}'$. A W*-algebra $\mathcal{Q}$ which contains the identity
operator, always designated by I, and is such that $\mathcal{Q} \cap \mathcal{Q}'$ consists
(only) of scalar multiples of I is called a <u>factor</u>. The term <u>Hilbert</u>
<u>space</u> will be used in the present paper to denote a complex (generalized)
Hilbert space of arbitrary dimension (> 0).

<u>Definition 2.2</u>. A <u>measure</u> <u>space</u> is the system composed of a set
R, a σ-ring $\mathcal{R}$ of subsets of R, and a countably-additive non-negative-
valued function r on $\mathcal{R}$. Such a space is <u>finite</u> if $R \in \mathcal{R}$ and $r(R)$
is finite. Such a space, denoted as $(R, \mathcal{R}, r)$, is called <u>regular</u> if R
is a locally compact topological space, $\mathcal{R}$ is the σ-ring generated by
the compact subsets of R, and if for every $S \in \mathcal{R}$, $r(S) = \text{L.U.B.}_{K \subset S} r(S)$
$= \text{G.L.B.}_{W \supset S} r(W)$, where K varies over the compact and W over the open
sets in $\mathcal{R}$. We denote such a space as (R, r), and a countably-additive
complex-valued function on $\mathcal{R}$ is called regular if the positive and nega-
tive constituents of its real and imaginary parts are such that the corresponding measure spaces are regular (i. e. are <u>regular</u> <u>measures</u>). A finite
measure space $(R, \mathcal{R}, r)$ is called <u>perfect</u> if it is regular, and if,
furthermore,   for every bounded measurable function on the space there is
a unique continuous function on R equal almost everywhere to the given

4   I. E. Segal

function.

     Definitions 2.3. A <u>state</u> of a C*-algebra $\mathcal{A}$ is a linear functional ω on $\mathcal{A}$ such that $\omega(U^*U) \geq 0$ and $\omega(U^*) = \bar{\omega}(U)$ for $U \in \mathcal{A}$ (a bar over a numerical-valued function denotes the complex-conjugate function), and with L.U.B. $_{\|U\| = 1,\ U \in \mathcal{A}}\, \omega(U^*U) = 1$. The <u>associated representation</u> φ of $\mathcal{A}$, <u>Hilbert space</u> $\mathcal{H}$, <u>canonical mapping</u> η of $\mathcal{A}$ into $\mathcal{H}$, and <u>wave function</u> z, are the essentially unique objects with the properties: 1) φ is a representation of $\mathcal{A}$ on $\mathcal{H}$ (i.e. it is a mapping on $\mathcal{A}$ to the operators on $\mathcal{H}$ which preserves algebraic operations, including that of adjunction); 2) η is continuous and linear on $\mathcal{A}$ to $\mathcal{H}$, $\eta(\mathcal{A})$ is dense in $\mathcal{H}$, and $(\eta(U), \eta(V)) = \omega(V^*U)$ for any U and V in $\mathcal{A}$; 3) $\varphi(U)\eta(V) = \eta(UV)$ for any U and V in $\mathcal{A}$; 4) z is an element of $\mathcal{H}$ of unit norm such that $\omega(U) = (\varphi(U)z, z)$ and $\eta(U) = Uz$ for $U \in \mathcal{A}$. (For further properties and an existence proof, see [8].) A representation φ of $\mathcal{A}$ on $\mathcal{H}$ is called <u>cyclic</u> if there exists an element z in $\mathcal{H}$ such that $\varphi(\mathcal{A})z$ is dense in $\mathcal{H}$; such an element z is called a <u>cyclic vector</u>.

     Definitions 2.4. The <u>spectrum</u> of a commutative (complex) Banach algebra is the topological space whose set is the collection of all continuous homomorphisms of the algebra into the complex numbers which are not identically zero, and whose topology is the weak topology in the conjugate space of the algebra. If Γ is a locally compact Hausdorff space, $C(\Gamma)$ (or $R(\Gamma)$) denotes the Banach algebra of all continuous complex-valued (or real-valued) functions on Γ which vanish at infinity on Γ (a function f on Γ vanishes at ∞ if for every positive number ε, the set $[\gamma \mid |f(\gamma)| \geq \varepsilon]$ is compact), with the norm of a function taken to be the maximum of its absolute value.

     Definition 2.5. If M is a measure space, $L_\alpha(M)$ denotes the

Banach space of αth-power integrable complex-valued functions on M, with
the usual norm, where $1 \leq \alpha \leq \infty$, $L_\infty(M)$ designating the Banach algebra
of all essentially bounded measurable functions on M. Two functions on a
measure space agree <u>nearly</u> <u>everywhere</u> (n. e.) if on every measurable set of
finite measure, they agree a. e., and a set in a measure space consists of
<u>nearly</u> <u>all</u> points of the space if the intersection of its complement with
any measurable set of finite measure has measure zero. If G is a locally
compact group, $L_\alpha(G)$ denotes $L_\alpha(G, m)$, where m is Haar measure on G.

3. <u>Decomposition</u> <u>of</u> <u>a</u> <u>state</u> <u>relative</u> <u>to</u> <u>a</u> <u>commutative</u> <u>algebra.</u>
We show in this section that any state of a C*-algebra $\mathcal{A}$ can be repre-
sented as an integral of more elementary states, over a measure space built
on the spectrum of a given commutative W*-algebra in $\mathcal{A}'$. By virtue of the
known correspondence between states and representations of C*-algebras
this shows, roughly speaking, that every cyclic representation (and hence
every representation) of $\mathcal{A}$ is a kind of direct integral of more elementary representations, in such a way that the integrals of the elementary
representation spaces are the invariant subspaces of the original representation space. Thus the present section could be described as an investi-
gation of the decomposition of a representation relative to a Boolean algebra of invariant subspaces.

In a later section the present decomposition, which involves no
measurability problems, as states are numerical-valued functions, is used
to treat direct integrals of Hilbert spaces (where the dimensionality may
vary from point to point) and of operator algebras (which vary similarly),
and thereby we avoid the measurability complications inherent in a direct
attack on such integrals. It will also be shown later that under suitable
hypotheses regarding $\mathcal{A}$ and the commutative algebra in question, the elementary representations which occur are almost everywhere irreducible.

In view of the correspondence between states and representations, it suffices to consider states ω of the form $\omega(T) = (Tz, z)$, where z is a cyclic vector for a. We mention also, as is pertinent to the decomposition of an algebra of the form C', where C is a commutative W*-algebra, that it is known that for any such algebra there exists a family $\{P_\mu\}$ of mutually disjoint projections in C such that the contraction of (the operators in) C' to $P_\mu \mathcal{H}$ has a cyclic vector; and that, moreover, if $\mathcal{H}$ is separable, then there always exists a cyclic vector for a itself.

THEOREM 1. __Let__ C __be a commutative W*-algebra on a Hilbert space__ $\mathcal{H}$, __let__ a __be a C*-algebra in__ C', __and let__ z __be a normalized cyclic vector for__ a. __Then there exists a weakly continuous map__ $\gamma \longrightarrow \omega_\gamma$ __on the spectrum__ Γ __of__ C __to the conjugate space of__ a __and a perfect measure__ μ __on__ Γ __such that: 1) for any__ $X \in a$ __and__ $S \in C$, $(SXz, z) = \int_\Gamma S(\gamma)\, \omega_\gamma(X)\, d\mu(\gamma)$, __where the mapping__ $S \longrightarrow S(\cdot)$ __is an isomorphism of__ C __onto the algebra of all complex-valued continuous functions on__ Γ; __2)__ ω_γ __is almost everywhere (relative to__ (Γ, μ)__) a state, and in case__ a __contains the identity operator, everywhere a state.__

The proof is based on a series of lemmas, mostly of a measure-theoretic character.

LEMMA 1.1. __Let__ (Γ, μ) __be a regular compact measure space, and let__ ψ __be a continuous linear functional on__ $C(\Gamma)$. __Then if__ ν __is the regular countably-additive set function on__ Γ __corresponding to__ ψ __(i.e.__ $\psi(f) = \int f(\gamma)\, d\nu(\gamma)$ __for__ $f \in C(\Gamma)$__), then for any Borel subset__ B __in__ Γ, __the variation of__ ν __over__ B __is__

$$\text{L.U.B.}_{f \in C(\Gamma),\ \|f\| = 1}\ \left| \int_B f(\gamma)\, d\nu(\gamma) \right|.$$

We recall the definition of the variation of ν, which is a numerical function on the Borel subsets of Γ denoted by $\text{Var } \nu$:

$(\mathrm{Var}\,\nu)(B) = $ L.U.B. $\sum_i |\nu(\Delta_i)|$ where $\{\Delta_i\}$ is an arbitrary finite collection of mutually disjoint Borel subsets of B. Now if $\int_B f(\gamma)d\mu(\gamma)$, with $f \in C(\Gamma)$, is approximated by sums $\sum_k f(\gamma_k)\mu(\Delta_k)$, then as the absolute value of this sum is bounded, when $\|f\| \leq 1$, by $\sum_k |\mu(\Delta_k)|$, it follows that $(\mathrm{Var}\,\mu)(B) \geq $ L.U.B. $[f \in C(\Gamma), \|f\| \leq 1] \; |\int_B f(\gamma)d\mu(\gamma)|$. On the other hand, in a regular locally compact measure space, it is plain that $\mathrm{Var}\,\mu$ can be defined by the equation $(\mathrm{Var}\,\mu)(B) = $ L.U.B. $\sum_i |\mu(K_i)|$, where $\{K_i\}$ is an arbitrary finite collection of mutually disjoint compact subsets of B. Now let ε be an arbitrary positive number, let $K_1, \cdots, K_n$ be mutually disjoint compact subsets of B such that $(\mathrm{Var}\,\mu)(B) \leq \sum_i |\mu(K_i)| + \varepsilon$, let Ω_i $(i = 1, \cdots, n)$ be mutually disjoint open subsets of Γ such that $\Omega_i \supset K_i$, and with $(\mathrm{Var}\,\mu)(\Omega_i - K_i) < \varepsilon n^{-1}$, and let f_i be an element of $C(\Gamma)$ which is 1 on K_i, 0 outside of Ω_i, and has values between 0 and 1 elsewhere. Setting $f(\gamma) = \sum_i f_i(\gamma)\overline{\mathrm{sgn}\,\mu(K_i)}$, then $\|f\| \leq 1$ and

$$\int_B f(\gamma)d\mu(\gamma) = \sum_i \int_{K_i} f_i(\gamma)\overline{\mathrm{sgn}\,\mu(K_i)}\, d\mu(\gamma) +$$

$$\sum_i \int_{B \cap (\Omega_i - K_i)} f_i(\gamma)\overline{\mathrm{sgn}\,\mu(K_i)}\,d\mu(\gamma) \; .$$

Now

$$\int_{K_i} f_i(\gamma)\overline{\mathrm{sgn}\,\mu(K_i)}\, d\mu(\gamma) = |\mu(K_i)|$$

and

$$|\int_{B \cap (\Omega_i - K_i)} f_i(\gamma)\overline{\mathrm{sgn}\,\mu(K_i)}\, d\mu(\gamma)| \leq (\mathrm{Var}\,\mu)(\Omega_i - K_i)$$

by the inequality obtained at the beginning of the proof. It results that $\sum_i |\mu(K_i)| \leq |\int_B f(\gamma)d\mu(\gamma)| + \varepsilon$, and hence that $(\mathrm{Var}\,\mu)(B) \leq |\int_B f(\gamma)\,d\mu(\gamma)| + 2\varepsilon$, which shows that $(\mathrm{Var}\,\mu)(B) \leq$ L.U.B.$_{f \in C(\Gamma), \|f\| = 1} \; |\int_B f(\gamma)\,d\mu(\gamma)|$.

LEMMA 1.2. _Let_ Γ _be a_ _compact Hausdorff space, and let_ ρ' _and_ σ' _be continuous linear functionals on_ $C(\Gamma)$ _such that_ ρ' _is real and non-negative on non-negative functions, and_ $|\sigma'(f)| \leq \alpha\, \rho'(|f|)$ _for all_ $f \in C(\Gamma)$ _and some fixed_ α . _If_ ρ _and_ σ _are the regular countably-additive set functions on_ Γ _corresponding to_ ρ' _and_ σ', _then_ σ _is absolutely continuous with respect to_ ρ. _Moreover, if in accordance with the Radon-Nikodym theorem we set_ $\sigma(B) = \int_B k(\gamma)\,d\rho(\gamma)$, _where_ B _is an arbitrary Borel subset of_ Γ , _and_ k _is a_ ρ-_integrable function, then_ $|k(\gamma)| \leq \alpha$ _almost everywhere with respect to_ ρ.

Let Δ be a compact subset of Γ on which ρ vanishes and let $\lambda = \rho + \operatorname{Var}\sigma$. Then λ is a regular measure on Γ and hence there exists a sequence $\{\Omega_n\}$ of open sets in Γ such that $\Omega_n \supset \Delta$, $\Omega_n \supset \Omega_{n+1}$, and $\lambda(\Omega_n) \longrightarrow \lambda(\Delta)$. Now let f_n be an element of $C(\Gamma)$ with values between 0 and 1, which is 1 on Δ and 0 outside of Ω_n . If χ_Δ is the characteristic function of Δ , it results that $f_n(\gamma) \longrightarrow \chi_\Delta(\gamma)$ a.e. with respect to λ , and hence a.e. with respect to ρ and $\operatorname{Var}\sigma$ also. By the Lebesgue convergence theorem, $\sigma(\Delta) = \lim_n \int f_n(\gamma)\,d\sigma(\gamma)$ and $|\sigma(\Delta)| = \lim_n |\sigma'(f_n)| \leq \alpha \limsup_n |\rho'(f_n)| = \alpha \limsup_n |\int f_n(\gamma)\,d\rho(\gamma)| = \alpha\,\rho(\Delta) = 0$.

Thus σ vanishes on any compact set on which ρ vanishes. Now let B be an arbitrary Borel subset of Γ for which $\rho(B) = 0$. By the regularity of σ there exists a sequence $\{K_1\}$ of compact subsets of Γ such that $K_1 \subset B$ and $\sigma(K_1) \longrightarrow \sigma(B)$. But $\sigma(K_1) = 0$ as $\rho(K_1) \leq \rho(B) = 0$, so $\sigma(B) = 0$.

It remains to show that $|k(\gamma)| \leq \alpha$ a.e. with respect to ρ. By Lemma 1.1, $(\operatorname{Var}\sigma)(B) = \text{L.U.B.}_{f \in C(\Gamma),\ \|f\| \leq 1} |\int_B f(\gamma)\,d\rho(\gamma)|$. Fixing B , let $\{K_n\}$ and $\{\Omega_n\}$ be sequences of compact and open subsets of Γ , respectively, such that $K_n \subset B \subset \Omega_n$ and $\lambda(\Omega_n - K_n) \longrightarrow 0$.

Then if h_n is a continuous function on Γ which is 1 on K_n, 0 outside of Ω_n, and between 0 and 1 elsewhere, $h_n(\gamma) \longrightarrow \chi_B(\gamma)$ a.e. with respect to λ and we have $|\int_\Gamma f(\gamma) h_n(\gamma)\, d\sigma(\gamma)| \longrightarrow |\int_B f(\gamma)\, d\sigma(\gamma)|$. Now $|\int_\Gamma f(\gamma) h_n(\gamma)\, d\sigma(\gamma)| = |\sigma'(fh_n)| \leq \alpha \rho'(|fh_n|) = \alpha \int_\Gamma |f(\gamma)| h_n(\gamma)\, d\rho(\gamma) \longrightarrow \alpha \int_B |f(\gamma)|\, d\rho(\gamma)$. It follows that if $f \epsilon C(\Gamma)$ and $\| f \| \leq 1$, then $|\int_B f(\gamma)\, d\sigma(\gamma)| \leq \alpha \rho(B)$, and hence $(\text{Var }\sigma)(B) \leq \alpha \rho(B)$. Now it is immediate from a well-known result that $(\text{Var }\sigma)(B) = \int_B |k(\gamma)|\, d\rho(\gamma)$, and setting $P_\epsilon = [\gamma |\ |k(\gamma)| \geq \alpha + \epsilon]$, where ϵ is a positive number, it results that $(\text{Var }\sigma)(P_\epsilon) \geq (\alpha + \epsilon)\, \rho(P_\epsilon)$. On the other hand, by the preceding argument, $(\text{Var }\sigma)(P_\epsilon) \leq \alpha \rho(P_\epsilon)$, so $(\alpha + \epsilon)\rho(P_\epsilon) \leq (\text{Var }\sigma)(P_\epsilon) \leq \alpha \rho(P_\epsilon)$. Hence $\rho(P_\epsilon) = 0$, and noting that $[\gamma |\ |h(\gamma)| > \alpha] = \bigcup_{n=1}^{\infty} P_{n^{-1}}$, it follows that $|k(\gamma)| \leq \alpha$ a.e. with respect to ρ.

LEMMA 1.3. <u>Let</u> (Γ, ρ) <u>be a compact regular measure space with the following properties</u>: 1) <u>if</u> $\{f_n\}$ <u>is a monotone decreasing sequence of non-negative continuous functions on</u> Γ, <u>then there exists a greatest lower bound</u> f <u>of the sequence in</u> $\mathcal{R}(\Gamma)$, <u>and</u> $\lim_n \int f_n(\gamma)\, d\rho(\gamma) = \int f(\gamma)\, d\rho(\gamma)$; 2) <u>the measure of any nonvoid open set is positive.</u> <u>Then</u> (Γ, ρ) <u>is a perfect measure space.</u>

Let K be a compact subset of Γ. Then there exists a sequence $\{f_n\}$ of non-negative-valued continuous functions on Γ such that $f_n \geq \chi_K$, $f_n(\gamma) \longrightarrow \chi_K(\gamma)$ a.e. with respect to ρ, and $f_n(\gamma) \geq f_{n+1}(\gamma)$, where χ_K is the characteristic function of K (such a sequence is readily constructed by induction, using the regular character of ρ). Now let f be the G.L.B. of the f_n in $\mathcal{R}(\Gamma)$. As $f_n(\gamma) \longrightarrow \chi_K(\gamma)$ a.e., $f(\gamma) \leq \chi_K(\gamma)$ a.e. On the other hand, $\int f(\gamma)\, d\rho(\gamma) = \lim_n \int f_n(\gamma)\, d\rho(\gamma) = \int \chi_K(\gamma)\, d\rho(\gamma)$, so that $\int (\chi_K(\gamma) - f(\gamma))\, d\rho(\gamma) = 0$, from which it follows without difficulty that $\chi_K(\gamma) = f(\gamma)$ a.e.

    Now let B be any Borel subset of Γ and let $\{K_i\}$ be a monotone increasing sequence of compact subsets of B such that $\rho(K_i) \longrightarrow \rho(B)$. Let $f_i \in \mathcal{R}(\Gamma)$ be such that $f_i(\gamma) = \chi_{K_i}(\gamma)$ a.e. Now it is easy to see from the fact that a nonvoid open subset of Γ has positive measure that the complement of a null set is dense. It follows that as $(f_i(\gamma))^2 = (\chi_{K_i}(\gamma))^2 = \chi_{K_i}(\gamma) = f_i(\gamma)$ a.e., for all γ $(f_i(\gamma))^2 = f_i(\gamma)$, so that $f_i(\gamma)$ is everywhere either 1 or 0. Similarly, if $i < j$, then $\chi_{K_i} \chi_{K_j} = \chi_{K_i}$, and it results that $f_i(\gamma)f_j(\gamma) = f_i(\gamma)$ a.e. so that $f_i f_j = f_i$. Hence the sequence $\{f_i\}$ is monotone increasing, and applying the first condition in the hypothesis of the lemma to the sequence $\{\chi_\Gamma - f_i\}$, it follows that the $\{f_i\}$ have a L.U.B. f in $\mathcal{R}(\Gamma)$, and that $\int f_i(\gamma)\,d\rho(\gamma) \longrightarrow \int f(\gamma)\,d\rho(\gamma)$. Since $f(\gamma) \geq f_i(\gamma)$, $f(\gamma) \geq \chi_{K_i}(\gamma)$ a.e., which implies that $f(\gamma) \geq \chi_{U_i K_i}(\gamma)$ a.e., or $f(\gamma) \geq \chi_B(\gamma)$ a.e. On the other hand, $\int f(\gamma)\,d\rho(\gamma) = \lim_n \int f_n(\gamma)\,d\rho(\gamma) = \lim_n \rho(K_n) = \rho(B) = \int \chi_B(\gamma)\,d\rho(\gamma)$, and it follows as in the preceding paragraph that $f(\gamma) = \chi_B(\gamma)$ a.e.

    Next let f be a bounded measurable function on (Γ, ρ). To prove the existence of an element of $C(\Gamma)$ which is equal a.e. to f it is clearly sufficient to consider the case in which f is real and nonnegative. If f is such, say $0 \leq f(\gamma) \leq \alpha$ for $\gamma \in \Gamma$, then defining $M_{i,n}$ to be the set $[\gamma \mid \alpha(1 - \frac{1}{2^n}) > f(\gamma) \geq \alpha(1 - \frac{i+1}{2^n})]$ ($i = 0, 1, 2, \cdots$), $M_{i,n}$ is a measurable set, and if $\chi_{i,n}$ is the characteristic function of $M_{i,n}$ and if $f_{i,n}$ is in $\mathcal{R}(\Gamma)$ and equal a.e. to $\chi_{i,n}$, then putting $f_n = \sum_{i=0}^{2^n} \alpha(1 - \frac{1}{2^n})f_{i,n}$, $f_n \in \mathcal{R}(\Gamma)$, and $|f(\gamma) - f_n(\gamma)| \leq \frac{\alpha}{2^n}$ a.e. and also $|f_{n+1}(\gamma) - f_n(\gamma)| \leq \frac{\alpha}{2^n}$ a.e. As the complement of a null set is dense, and as $f_{n+1} - f_n$ is in $C(\Gamma)$, the last inequality holds for all γ. It follows that $\sum_{n=1}^{\infty} (f_{n+1}(\gamma)-f_n(\gamma))$ is uniformly convergent, so that f_n converges uniformly, say to f', an element of $\mathcal{R}(\Gamma)$. It is plain that $f' = f$ a.e. If there were two elements of $C(\Gamma)$ equal a.e. to f, then we would have a continuous function (their difference) equal a.e. to zero, and by an earlier remark zero everywhere.

LEMMA 1.4. <u>With the notation of the theorem, let μ be the regular measure on</u> Γ <u>such that</u> $(Tz, z) = \int_{\Gamma} T(\gamma)\, d\mu(\gamma)$ <u>for</u> $T \in C$. <u>Then</u> (Γ, μ) <u>is a perfect measure space.</u>

Observe first that the measure of a nonvoid open subset of Γ is positive. For if Ω is a nonvoid open set of measure zero, let K be any nonvoid compact subset, and let f be an element of $\mathcal{R}(\Gamma)$ which is 1 on K, 0 outside Ω, and between 0 and 1 elsewhere. Then f^2 vanishes outside Ω, so that $\int (f(\gamma))^2\, d\mu(\gamma) = 0$. It follows that if F is the operator in C which corresponds to f, then $(F^2 z, z) = 0 = \| Fz \|^2$, and hence $Fz = 0$. Now if X is an arbitrary element of $\mathcal{A}$, we have $XFz = 0 = FXz$. Now $[Xz \mid X \in \mathcal{A}]$ is dense in $\mathcal{H}$, and thus F vanishes on a dense set; being continuous, it must vanish identically. Hence $f = 0$, a contradiction.

It remains only to show that the hypothesis of Lemma 1.3 regarding monotone sequences of functions in $\mathcal{R}(\Gamma)$ is valid. Let $\{f_n\}$ be a monotone decreasing sequence of non-negative continuous functions on Γ, and let F_n be the operator in C which corresponds to f_n. As C is algebraically isomorphic to $C(\Gamma)$ (in an adjoint-preserving fashion), its subring $\mathcal{R}$ of self-adjoint elements is order-isomorphic to $\mathcal{R}(\Gamma)$, and we have $F_n \geq F_{n+1}$, $F_n \geq 0$. Obviously the F_n commute with each other and by a known result in the theory of Hilbert space, the strong limit of the sequence $\{F_n\}$ exists, say $\lim_n F_n x = Fx$ for $x \in \mathcal{H}$. If

12   I. E. Segal

f is the element of $C(\Gamma)$ corresponding to F, from the inequality $F_n \geq F$ we have $f_n \geq f$. Now if $h \in \mathcal{R}(\Gamma)$ and $f_n \geq h$ for all n, then $F_n \geq H$ for all n, where H is the element of $\mathcal{R}$ corresponding to h. This would imply that $(F_n x, x) \geq (Hx, x)$ for $x \in \mathcal{H}$, and taking $\lim_n$ on both sides of this inequality yields the inequality $(Fx, x) \geq (Hx, x)$. This means that $F \geq H$, so that $f \geq h$, and hence f is the G.L.B. of the f_n. Moreover, we have $\lim_n \int f_n(\gamma)\, d\mu(\gamma) = \lim_n (F_n z, z) = (Fz, z) = \int f(\gamma)\, d\mu(\gamma)$.

LEMMA 1.5. *If* ω *is a state of a C*-algebra containing a normal operator* S, *then* $|\omega(S)| \leq \omega(|S|)$.

We explain that $|S|$ is the absolute-value function, applied to S by the usual operational calculus. The C*-algebra generated by S is isomorphic to the algebra of all continuous complex-valued functions vanishing at infinity on some locally compact Hausdorff space Ξ. By the Riesz-Markoff theorem, $\omega(T) = \int_{\Xi} t(\xi)\, d\sigma(\xi)$, for all T in that algebra, $t(\xi)$ being the corresponding element of $C(\Xi)$ and σ being a regular measure on Ξ. Putting s for the element of $C(\Xi)$ corresponding to S, we have $\omega(S) = \int_{\Xi} s(\xi)\, d\sigma(\xi)$ and hence $|\omega(S)| \leq \int_{\Xi} |s(\xi)|\, d\sigma(\xi) = \omega(|S|)$.

PROOF OF THEOREM. We first prove the theorem for the case in which $\mathcal{Q}$ contains the identity operator I. Let ω be the state of $\mathcal{Q}$ defined by the equation $\omega(X) = (Xz, z)$, $X \in \mathcal{Q}$. Then $\omega(SX)$, as a function of $S \in C$ for fixed $X \in \mathcal{Q}$, is clearly linear, and it is bounded for $|\omega(SX)| \leq \|SX\| \leq \|S\|\,\|X\|$. This linear functional induces, via the correspondence between C and $C(\Gamma)$ a bounded linear functional on $C(\Gamma)$, and by the known form for such a linear functional we have $\omega(SX) = \int_\Gamma S(\gamma)\, d\mu_X(\gamma)$, for some unique countably-additive regular set function on Γ, μ_X. We observe next that $|\omega(SX)| \leq \alpha\, \omega(|S|)$ for

$X \in \mathcal{Q}$ and $S \in C$, where $\alpha = \| X_1 \| + \| X_2 \|$, $X = X_1 + iX_2$, X_1 and X_2 being SA. For $|\omega(SX)| = |\omega(SX_1) + i\omega(SX_2)| \leq |\omega(SX_1)| + |\omega(SX_2)|$; since the X_j $(j = 1, 2)$, S, and their adjoints mutually commute, $X_j S$ is normal so by Lemma 1.5 $|\omega(SX_j)| \leq \omega(|SX_j|)$. Now the C*-algebra generated by X_j and S is algebraically isomorphic to $C(\overline{\Xi}_j)$ for some locally compact Hausdorff space $\overline{\Xi}_j$, and it is easy to deduce from this that $|SX_j| = |S| |X_j| \leq \| X_j \| |S|$. It follows that $|\omega(SX_j)| \leq \omega(\| X_j \| |S|)$, and the stated inequality follows.

Hence Lemma 1.2 applies and asserts that μ_X is absolutely continuous with respect to $\mu = \mu_I$, and that if we write (by the Radon-Nikodym theorem) $\mu_X(B) = \int_B k_X(\gamma) \, d\mu(\gamma)$, B being an arbitrary Borel subset of Γ, then k_X is essentially bounded with respect to μ. Now by Lemma 1.4, (Γ, μ) is perfect and hence there exists a unique continuous function $k_X'(\gamma)$ on Γ which coincides a.e. with respect to μ, with $k_X(\gamma)$. Defining ω_γ as the functional on $\mathcal{Q}$ given by the equation $\omega_\gamma(X) = k_X'(\gamma)$, then for each $X \in \mathcal{Q}$, $\omega_\gamma(X)$ is a continuous function of γ. Now as $\omega(SX)$ is linear in X for fixed S, μ_X is a linear function of X, and it follows that $k_{X+Y}'(\gamma) = k_X'(\gamma) + k_Y'(\gamma)$ a.e. on (Γ, μ) for any X and Y in $\mathcal{Q}$. Hence $k_{X+Y}'(\gamma) = k_X'(\gamma) + k_Y'(\gamma)$ a.e., but as both sides of this equation represent continuous functions of γ, by a familiar argument we have equality everywhere. In a similar fashion it follows that for any complex number β, $k_{\beta X}'(\gamma) = \beta k_X'(\gamma)$ for all $\gamma \in \Gamma$. These results mean that for each γ, ω_γ is a linear functional on $\mathcal{Q}$. Since the product of two commuting SA nonnegative operators is a SA nonnegative operator, $\omega(SX)$ is a positive linear functional, of S, for fixed SA non-negative X, and hence μ_X is then a measure. It follows that for such X, $k_X(\gamma)$ is a.e. nonnegative, so $k_X'(\gamma)$ is everywhere nonnegative, and the same is true of $\omega_\gamma(X)$. To show that ω_γ is for each γ a state of $\mathcal{Q}$ it remains

I. E. Segal

only to show that $\omega_\gamma(I) = 1$ for all γ. Now $(Sz, z) = \int S(\gamma) d\mu(\gamma) = \int S(\gamma) \omega_\gamma(I) d\mu(\gamma)$, so $\int S(\gamma) \{1 - \omega_\gamma(I)\} d\mu(\gamma) = 0$, for all $S \in C$. As S ranges over C, $S(\cdot)$ ranges over all continuous, and so, as (Γ, μ) is perfect, all bounded measurable, complex-valued functions on Γ, and therefore $\omega_\gamma(I) = 1$ a.e., but as $\omega_\gamma(I)$ is a continuous function of γ we have equality everywhere. This completes the proof for the case $I \in Q$, for the continuity of ω_γ as a function of γ with values in the conjugate space of Q is equivalent to the continuity of $\omega_\gamma(X)$ as a function of γ for all $X \in Q$.

Now suppose that I is not necessarily in Q, and let Q_1 be the algebra obtained by adjoining I to Q; it is not difficult to see that Q_1 is a C*-algebra. Then $Q_1 \subset C'$ and by what has just been proved there exists a continuous map $\gamma \longrightarrow \omega'_\gamma$ on Γ to the state space of Q_1 (i.e., the collection of all states of Q_1 topologized by the weak topology on its conjugate space) such that for $X \in Q_1$ and $S \in C$, $(SXz, z) = \int_\Gamma S(\gamma) \, \omega'_\gamma(X) \, d\mu(\gamma)$. It remains only to show that the contraction ω_γ of ω'_γ to Q is a.e. a state, for it is clear that the mapping $\gamma \longrightarrow \omega_\gamma$ is continuous on Γ to the conjugate space of Q. Let $\{V_\mu\}$ be an "approximate identity" for Q (cf. [8]), i.e., $\|V_\mu\| \leq 1$ for all μ, $V_\mu \in Q$, and $V_\mu X \longrightarrow X$ for all $X \in Q$. Then for any X and Y in Q, $(V_\mu Xz, V_\mu Yz) \longrightarrow (Xz, Yz)$. Thus the equation $(V_\mu x, V_\mu y) \longrightarrow (x, y)$ holds for a dense set of x and y in $\mathcal{H}$, and as $\|V_\mu\|$ is bounded, it must consequently hold for all x and y in $\mathcal{H}$. In particular $(V_\mu z, V_\mu z) \longrightarrow (z, z)$, and so there exists a sequence $\{U_n\}$ in Q (a subsequence of the V_μ) such that $\|U_n\| \leq 1$ and $(U_n z, U_n z) \longrightarrow 1$. It follows from an equation above that $\int_\Gamma \omega_\gamma(U_n^* U_n) \, d\mu(\gamma) \longrightarrow 1$, or $\int_\Gamma (1 - \omega_\gamma(U_n^* U_n)) \, d\mu(\gamma) \longrightarrow 0$. As $1 - \omega_\gamma(U_n^* U_n) \geq 0$, the sequence of functions of γ, $\{1 - \omega_\gamma(U_n^* U_n)\}$ converges to zero in $L_1(\Gamma, \mu)$. If $\{U_{n_i}\}$ is a subsequence such that

$1 - \omega_\gamma(U_{n_1}^* U_{n_1}) \longrightarrow 0$ a.e. on (Γ, μ), then we have $\text{L.U.B.}_1 \, \omega_\gamma(U_{n_1}^* U_{n_1}) = 1$ a.e., which shows that ω_γ is a state a.e.

4. <u>Direct integrals of Hilbert spaces</u>. In this section we define and treat direct integrals of Hilbert spaces, and show that every state decomposition such as that of the preceding section gives rise to this kind of direct integral. In this way an arbitrary C*-algebra $\mathcal{A}$ can be decomposed with respect to any commutative W*-algebra in $\mathcal{A}'$ (or alternatively, with respect to any Boolean algebra of closed invariant subspaces). Our definition of direct integral is somewhat similar to that given by von Neumann [16], but we find it necessary to consider two types of integrals, a "strong" and a "weak" type, whose relationship is analogous to that of strong and weak integrals of vector-valued functions.

<u>Definition 4.1.</u>   Let $(R, \mathcal{R}, r)$ be a measure space M, and suppose that for each point $p \in R$ there is a Hilbert space $\mathcal{H}_p$. A Hilbert space $\mathcal{H}$ is called a <u>direct integral</u> of the $\mathcal{H}_p$ over M (symbolically $\mathcal{H} = \int_R \mathcal{H}_p \, dr(p)$) if for each $x \in \mathcal{H}$ there is a function $x(p)$ on R to $\bigcup_{p \in R} \mathcal{H}_p$, such that $x(p) \in \mathcal{H}_p$, and with the following properties (1) and either 2a) or 2b)): 1) if x and y are in $\mathcal{H}$ and if $z = \alpha x + \beta y$, then $(x(p), y(p))$ is integrable on M, $(x, y) = \int_R (x(p), y(p)) \, dr(p)$, and $z(p) = \alpha x(p) + \beta y(p)$ for almost all $p \in R$; 2) if $z(p) \in H_p$ for all p, if $(x(p), z(p))$ is measurable for all $x \in \mathcal{H}$, and if $(z(p), z(p))$ is integrable on M, then there exists an element z' of $\mathcal{H}$ such that

    a) $z'(p) = z(p)$ almost everywhere on M, or

    b) $(z'p), x(p)) = (z(p), x(p))$ almost everywhere on M, $x \in \mathcal{H}$.

The integral is called <u>strong</u> or <u>weak</u> according as 2a) or 2b) holds. The function $x(p)$ is called the <u>decomposition</u> of x, and we use the following notation for this: $x = \int_R x(p)\, dr\,(p)$.

A linear operator T on $\mathcal{H}$ is said to be decomposable with respect to the preceding direct integral if there is a function $T(p)$ on R to $\bigcup_{p \in R} \mathcal{B}_p$, where $\mathcal{B}_p$ is the collection of all bounded linear operators on $\mathcal{H}_p$, such that $T(p) \in \mathcal{B}_p$ for all p and with the property that for all x and y in $\mathcal{H}$, $(T(p)\, x(p),\, y(p))$ is integrable on M and $\int_R (T(p)\, x(p),\, y(p))\, dr(p) = (Tx,\, y)$. The function $T(p)$ is then called the <u>decomposition</u> of T, and we symbolize this situation by the notation $T = \int_R T(p)\, dr(p)$. If $T(p)$ is almost everywhere a scalar operator, T is called <u>diagonalizable</u>.

The basic theorem of this section asserts that a state decomposition such as that of the preceding section induces a decomposition of the Hilbert space as a direct integral, in which every element of $\mathcal{Q}$ is decomposable, and in which the diagonalizable elements are exactly those in $\mathcal{C}$. Before giving a precise statement of this theorem we make two remarks. First, it is not difficult to show that in case $\mathcal{H}$ is separable, a weak direct integral becomes an essentially equivalent strong one when the $\mathcal{H}_p$ are replaced by appropriate closed linear subspaces of themselves. Second, the analog, of condition 2b for direct integrals of spaces, in the case of direct integration of operators, is valid without further assumption: if $T(p) \in \mathcal{B}_p$ for all p, if $\| T(p) \|$ is essentially bounded on M, and if the integral $\int_R (T(p)\, x(p),\, y(p))\, dr(p)$ exists for all x and y in $\mathcal{H}$, then there exists an (obviously unique) bounded linear operator T such that $(Tx,\, y) = \int (T(p)\, x(p),\, y(p))\, dr(p)$ for all x and y in $\mathcal{H}$. For setting $Q(x,\, y) = \int (T(p)\, x(p),\, y(p))\, dr(p)$, it is clear that Q is conjugate-bilinear (linear in x and conjugate-linear in y), and that, setting $\alpha = \text{ess sup}_{p \in R} \| T(p) \|$, $|Q(x,\, y)| \leq \int |(T(p)\, x(p),\, y(p))|\, dr(p) \leq \int \alpha \| x(p) \|\, \| y(p) \|\, dr(p) \leq \alpha \left\{ (\int \| x(p) \|^2\, dr(p))\, (\int \| y(p) \|^2\, dr(p)) \right\}^{1/2} = \alpha \| x \|\, \| y \|$, so Q is bounded. It follows readily from the Riesz representation theorem for linear functionals on $\mathcal{H}$ that an operator T with the stated property exists.

THEOREM 2. _Let_ Q, C, _and_ z _be as in Theorem 1, and let_ $M = (R, \mathcal{R}, r)$ _be a measure space with the properties:_ 1) C _is algebraically isomorphic (in a fashion taking adjoints into complex conjugates) with the algebra of all complex-valued bounded measurable on_ M, _the element_ S _of_ C _corresponding to the function_ $S(.)$; 2) _for each_ $p \in R$ _there is a state_ ω_p _of_ Q, _and for_ $T \in Q$, $\omega_p(T)$ _is measurable on_ M; 3) _for_ $T \in Q$ _and_ $S \in C$, $(STz, z) = \int_R \omega_p(T) S(p) dr(p)$.

Then if $\mathcal{H}_p$, φ_p, η_p, _and_ z_p _are the representation space, representation of_ Q, _canonical map of_ Q _into_ $\mathcal{H}_p$, _and wave function, respectively, associated with_ ω_p, _we have weakly, and in case_ Q _is separable in the uniform topology, strongly,_ $\mathcal{H} = \int_R \mathcal{H}_p \, dr(p)$ _in such a way that for_ $U \in Q$, $U = \int_R \varphi_p(U) dr(p)$, _and_ $Uz = \int_R \eta_p(U) dr(p)$. _Every operator decomposable with respect to this direct integral is in_ C', _and an operator is diagonalizable if and only if it is in_ C.

We begin by defining $x(p)$ (more precisely, a residue class of the space of functions on R to $\bigcup_p \mathcal{H}_p$, with $x(p) \in \mathcal{H}_p$ for all p, modulo the linear subspace of functions a.e. zero), for x of the form Uz, by the equation $x(p) = \eta_p(U)$. To see that $x(p)$ is single-valued, suppose that $Uz = Vz$, with U and V in Q. Then $Wz = 0$, where $W = U - V$, so $(Wz, Wz) = 0$, but by 3) in the hypothesis, $(Wz, Wz) = (W*Wz, z)$ $= \int_R \omega_p(W*W) dr(p) = 0$. Now $\omega_p(W*W) \geq 0$ for all p, so that the last equation implies $\omega_p(W*W) = 0$ a.e. This means that $(\eta_p(W), \eta_p(W)) = 0$ a.e., or $\eta_p(W) = 0$ a.e. on R, and hence $x(.)$ is unique (modulo the subspace mentioned).

Now let x be arbitrary in $\mathcal{H}$ and let $\{U_n\}$ be a sequence in Q such that $U_n z \longrightarrow x$. Then $\| U_n z - U_m z \| \longrightarrow 0$ as $m, n \longrightarrow \infty$, and

$$||U_n z - U_m z||^2 = ((U_n - U_m)*(U_n - U_m)z,z) = \int \omega_p((U_n - U_m)*(U_n - U_m))\, dr(p)$$

$= \int ||\eta_p(U_n) - \eta_p(U_m)||^2\, dr(p) \longrightarrow 0$. We now apply the procedure utilized in the proof of the Riesz-Fischer theorem to the selection of a subsequence of $\{\eta_p(U_n)\}$ whose limit exists a. e. and defines the function which we shall designate as $x(p)$. Let $\{n_i\}$ be a subsequence of the positive integers such that $n_{i+1} > n_i$, and with $\int ||\eta_p(U_n) - \eta_p(U_m)||^2\, dr(p) < 8^{-1}$ for n and m greater than n_i. The set of p's for which $||\eta_p(U_{n_i}) - \eta_p(U_{n_{i+1}})|| > \mathcal{E}$ is, for $\mathcal{E} > 0$, clearly of measure less than $\mathcal{E}^{-2}\, 8^{-1}$, and taking $\mathcal{E} = 2^{-1}$, it results that $||\eta_p(U_{n_i}) - \eta_p(U_{n_{i+1}})|| \leq 2^{-1}$ except on a set of measure less than 2^{-1}. Therefore the inequalities $||\eta_p(U_{n_i}) - \eta_p(U_{n_{i+1}})|| \leq 2^{-i}$ hold simultaneously for all $i > j$ except on a set D_j of measure less than $\sum_{i>j} 2^{-i} = 2^{-j+1}$. It follows that the series $\sum_{i=1}^{\infty} \{\eta_p(U_{n_i}) - \eta_p(U_{n_{i+1}})\}$ is uniformly convergent for $p \notin D_j$, and hence that $\lim_i \eta_p(U_{n_i})$ exists uniformly for $p \notin D_j$. Putting $x(p)$ for that limit, it is clear from the fact that $r(D_j) \longrightarrow 0$ as $j \longrightarrow \infty$ that the limit exists a. e. so that $x(p)$ is defined a. e. (and may be defined arbitrari the null set on which the limit fails to exist).

From the equation $\int_R ||\eta_p - \eta_p(U_{n_j})||^2 dr(p) < 8^{-1}$ for m and $n_j > n_i$, it results that $\int_{R-D_k} ||\eta_p(U_m) - \eta_p(U_{n_j})||^2 dr(p) < 8^{-1}$ for m and n_j greater than n_i, and for any k. Now $\eta_p(U_{n_j})$ converges uniformly to $x(p)$ as $j \longrightarrow \infty$, on $R-D_k$, so $\int_{R-D_k} ||\eta_p(U_m) - x(p)||^2 dr(p) \leq 8^{-1}$ for $m > n_i$, and for any k. Letting $k \longrightarrow \infty$, it follows that $\int_R ||\eta_p(U_m) - x(p)||^2 dr(p) \leq 8^{-1}$ if $m > n_i$ so $\int ||\eta_p(U_m) - x(p)||^2 dr(p) \longrightarrow 0$ as $m \longrightarrow \infty$.

We show next that the function $x(p)$ is independent of the sequence $\{U_n\}$ utilized. Suppose that $\{U_n'\}$ is a sequence in Q such that $U_n' z \longrightarrow x$, and let $x'(p)$ be a function obtained from $\{U_n'\}$ in the same fashion as that in which $x(p)$ was obtained from $\{U_n\}$. Then $\int_R ||\eta_p(U_m') - x'(p)||^2 dr(p) \longrightarrow 0$ as $m \longrightarrow \infty$. Thus both

$\{\| \eta_p(U_m) - x(p) \|^2\}$ and $\{\| \eta_p(U'_m) - x'(p) \|^2\}$ converge to zero $L_1(M)$.

Now $\int_R \| \eta_p(U_m) - \eta_p(U'_m) \|^2 \, dr(p) = \| U_m z - U'_m z \|^2 \longrightarrow 0$ as $m \longrightarrow \infty$, so

that $\{\| \eta_p(U_m) - \eta_p(U'_m) \|^2\}$ also converges to zero in $L_1(M)$. Choosing

a common subsequence $\{m_i\}$ such that the corresponding subsequences of all

three sequences converge a.e., we have $\| x(p) - x'(p) \| \leq$

$\| x(p) - \eta_p(U_{m_i}) \| + \| \eta_p(U_{m_i}) - \eta_p(U'_{m_i}) \| + \| \eta_p(U'_{m_i}) - x'(p) \|$ so that

$\| x(p) - x'(p) \| = 0$ a.e., i.e., $x(p) = x'(p)$ a.e.

If y is any element in $\mathcal{H}$ and if $V_n z \longrightarrow y$ with $V_n \in \mathcal{Q}$,

let $\{V_{n_i}\}$ be a subsequence such that $\eta_p(V_{m_i}) \longrightarrow y(p)$ a.e. Then a.e.

we have $(x(p), y(p)) = \lim_{i,j} (\eta_p(U_{n_i}), \eta_p(V_{m_j}))$, and

$(\eta_p(U_{n_i}), \eta_p(V_{m_j})) = \omega_p(V^*_{m_j} U_{n_i})$, which is a measurable function of p.

Thus $(x(p), y(p))$ is a.e. the limit of a sequence of measurable functions,

and is hence itself measurable. Moreover, $(x(p), y(p))$ is integrable

and has (x, y) for its integral. To show the integrability, it suffices

to show that $(x(p), y(p))$ is the limit in $L_1(M)$ of the integrable

functions $(\eta_p(U_{n_i}), \eta_p(V_{m_j}))$, as $i, j \longrightarrow \infty$. Now $(x(p), y(p)) -$

$(\eta_p(U_{n_i}), \eta_p(V_{m_j})) = \{(x(p), y(p)) - (\eta_p(U_{n_i}), y(p))\} +$

$(\eta_p(U_{n_i}), y(p)) - (\eta_p(U_{n_i}), \eta_p(V_{m_j}))\}$, so that the left side of this

equation is bounded by $\| x(p) - \eta_p(U_{n_i}) \| \, \| y(p) \| + \| \eta_p(U_{n_i}) \| \, \| y(p) -$

$\eta_p(U_{n_j}) \|$. Hence, applying Schwarz' inequality,

$\int |(x(p), y(p)) - (\eta_p(U_{n_i}), \eta_p(V_{m_j})| \, dr(p) \leq$

$\left\{ \int \| x(p) - \eta_p(U_{n_i}) \|^2 \, dr(p) \int \| y(p) \|^2 \, dr(p) \right\}^{1/2} +$

$\left\{ \int \| \eta_p(U_{n_i}) \|^2 \, dr(p) \int \| y(p) - \eta_p(U_{n_j}) \|^2 \, dr(p) \right\}^{1/2}$. Now $y(p) =$

$y(p) - \eta_p(U_{m_j}) + \eta_p(U_{m_j})$, so $\| y(p) \| \leq \| y(p) - \eta_p(U_{m_j}) \| +$

$\| \eta_p(U_{n_j}) \|$. By Minkowski's inequality, $\int \| y(p) \|^2 \, dr(p) \leq$

$\left\{ \int \| y(p) - \eta_p(U_{n_j}) \|^2 \, dr(p) \right\}^{1/2} + \left\{ \int \| \eta_p(U_{n_j}) \|^2 \, dr(p) \right\}^{1/2}$, which shows

that $\| y(p) \|^2$ is integrable. Also, $\int \| \eta_p(U_{n_i}) \|^2 \, dr(p) =$

$\int \omega_p(U_{n_i}^* U_{n_i}) \, dr(p) = (U_{n_i}^* U_{n_i} z, z) = \| U_{n_i} z \|^2$, which is bounded as $i \longrightarrow$

∞ . It is easy to conclude that $\int | (x(p), y(p)) - (\eta_p(U_{n_i}), \eta_p(V_{m_j}) |$

$dr(p) \longrightarrow 0$ as $i, j \longrightarrow \infty$. This shows that $(x(p), y(p))$ is integrable

and that its integral is $\lim_{i,j} \int (\eta_p(U_{n_i}), \eta_p(V_{m_j})) \, dr(p) =$

$\lim_{i,j} \int \omega_p(V_{m_j}^* U_{n_i}) \, dr(p) = \lim_{i,j} (U_{n_i} z, V_{m_j} z) = (x, y)$. That $x(.)$ is

a linear function of x is clear from the fact that $\alpha \eta_p(U_{n_i}) +$

$\beta \eta_p(V_{m_j})$ on the one hand converges a.e. as $i \longrightarrow \infty$ to $\alpha x(p) + \beta y(p)$,

and on the other, equals $\eta_p(\alpha U_{n_i} + \beta V_{m_j})$, of which a subsequence con-

verges a.e. to $(\alpha x + \beta y)(p)$ (for $(\alpha U_{n_i} + \beta V_{m_j}) z \longrightarrow \alpha x + \beta y$ as

$i, j \longrightarrow \infty$).

      Before concluding the proof that $\mathcal{H}$ is the direct integral of

the $\mathcal{H}_p$, we consider the decomposition of operators. Let T, U, and V be

arbitrary in $\mathcal{A}$. Then $(TUz, Vz) = (V^* TUz, z) = \int \omega_p(V^* TU) \, dr(p) =$

$\int (\eta_p(TU), \eta_p(V)) \, dr(p) = \int (\varphi_p(T) \eta_p(U), \eta_p(V)) \, dr(p)$. This shows

that the equation $(Tx, y) = \int (\varphi_p(T) x(p), y(p)) \, dr(p)$ holds for x and

y of the forms $x = Uz$, $y = Vz$. Now let x be arbitrary in $\mathcal{H}$ and let

$x_n \longrightarrow x$, where $\{x_n\}$ is a sequence in $\mathcal{A}z$. Then if $y = Vz$, we have

$(Tx_n, y) = \int (\varphi_p(T) x_n(p), y(p)) \, dr(p)$ and

$|\int(\varphi_p(T) x_n(p), y(p)) \, dr(p) - \int(\varphi_p(T) x(p), y(p)) \, dr(p)| =$
$|\int(\varphi_p(T) x_n(p) - x(p), y(p)) \, dr(p)|, = D$ say. Now
$|(\varphi_p(T)(x_n(p) - x(p)), y(p))| \leq \|\varphi_p(T)\| \; \|x_n(p) - x(p)\| \; \|y(p)\|$, and
$\|\varphi_p(T)\| \leq \|T\|$, as this is true for any representation, so $D \leq$
$\|T\| \; \|x_n(p) - x(p)\| \; \|y(p)\| \, dr(p) \leq \|T\| \left\{\int \|x_n(p) - x(p)\|^2 \, dr(p)\right\}^{1/2}$
$\left\{\int \|y(p)\|^2 \, dr(p)\right\}^{1/2}$, which has the limit zero as $n \longrightarrow \infty$. On the
other hand, it is plain that $(Tx_n, y) \longrightarrow (Tx, y)$, so in this case we likewise have $(Tx, y) = \int(\varphi_p(T) x(p), y(p)) \, dr(p)$. Next let y be arbi-
trary in $\mathcal{H}$, let $\{y_n\}$ be a sequence in $\mathcal{U}z$ with $y_n \longrightarrow y$. Then esti-
mating $|\int \varphi_p(T) x(p), y_n(p)) \, dr(p) - \int \varphi_p(T) x(p), y(p)) \, dr(p)|$ as in
the case of a similar expression above, it results that the present expres-
sion has the limit zero as $n \longrightarrow \infty$. It follows that the preceding
formula for (Tx, y) is valid for arbitrary x and y in $\mathcal{H}$.

Now suppose that $T \in \mathcal{U}$ and $S \in \mathcal{C}$. We shall show that (STx, y)
$= \int S(p) (\varphi_p(T) x(p), y(p)) \, dr(p)$ and that $(Sx, y) =$
$\int S(p) (x(p), y(p)) \, dr(p)$, for all x and y in $\mathcal{H}$. For $x = Uz$ and
$y = Vz$, the equation $(STx, y) = \int S(p) (\varphi_p(T) x(p), y(p)) \, dr(p)$ follows
trivially from the hypothesis. Now if x and y are arbitrary in $\mathcal{H}$,
and if $\{x_n\}$ and $\{y_n\}$ are sequences in $\mathcal{U}z$ which converge respectively
to x and to y, then $(STx, y) = \lim_n (STx_n, y_n) =$
$\lim_n \int S(p) (\varphi_p(T) x_n(p), y_n(p)) \, dr(p)$. Now $S(p)$ is bounded as a function of p, and this observation together with an argument used above in a
similar situation shows that $\int S(p) (\varphi_p(T) x_n(p), y_n(p)) \, dr(p) \longrightarrow$
$\int S(p) (\varphi_p(T) x(p), y(p)) \, dr(p)$, as $n \longrightarrow \infty$. Again, if $x = Uz$ with
$U \in \mathcal{U}$ and $y \in \mathcal{H}$, and putting $\{W_\mu\}$ for an approximate identity for
$\mathcal{U}$, we have $(SW_\mu x, y) = \int S(p) (\varphi_p(W_\mu) x(p), y(p)) \, dr(p) = (SW_\mu Uz, y)$
$= \int S(p) (\varphi_p(W_\mu U) z(p), y(p)) \, dr(p)$. Since $\varphi_p(W_\mu U) \longrightarrow \varphi_p(U)$
uniformly, relative to μ, i.e., $\|\varphi_p(W_\mu U) - \varphi_p(U)\| \longrightarrow 0$ uniformly
on R, so that a sequence $\{\mu_1\}$ exists such that $\varphi_p(W_{\mu_1} U) \longrightarrow \varphi_p(U)$

uniformly relative to i, the last expression converges to
$\int S(p) (\varphi_p(U) z(p), y(p)) dr(p) = \int S(p) (x(p), y(p)) dr(p)$. Now, if x
and y are both arbitrary in $\mathcal{H}$, let $\{x_n\}$ be a sequence in Qz which
converges to x. Then $(Sx, y) = \lim_n (Sx_n, y) = \lim_n$
$\int S(p) (x_n(p), y(p)) dr(p)$, which last expression is readily seen to equal
$\int S(p) (x(p), y(p)) dr(p)$. We observe finally that $(Sx)(p) = S(p) x(p)$
a.e., for $\int ((Sx) (p) - S(p) x(p),(Sx)(p) - S(p) x(p)) dr(p) =$
$\int \{((Sx)(p), (Sx)(p)) - (S(p) x(p), (Sx)(p)) - ((Sx)(p), S(p) x(p)) +$
$(S(p) x(p), S(p) x(p))\} dr(p) = (Sx, Sx) - (Sx, Sx) - (S*(Sx), x) +$
$((S*S)x, x) = 0$ (the assumption that the integral exists being justified
by the given expansion of the integrand).

　　We now conclude the proof that $\mathcal{H}$ is a direct integral of the
$\mathcal{H}_p$. Suppose that $w'(p)$ is a function on R such that $w'(p) \in \mathcal{H}_p$ for
$p \in R$, $(W'(p), w'(p))$ is integrable on M, and with $(x(p), w'(p))$ measurable on M for all $x \in \mathcal{H}$. Then $(x(p), w'(p))$ is integrable on M, for
by two applications of Schwarz' inequality we have
$$\int |(x(p), w'(p))| dr(p) \leq \int \| x(p) \| \; \| w'(p) \| dr(p) \leq$$
$$\left\{ \int \| x(p) \|^2 dr(p) \int \| w'(p) \|^2 dr(p) \right\}^{1/2} .$$
The same inequality shows that setting $L(x) = \int (x(p), w'(p)) dr(p)$, then
L is a continuous linear functional on $\mathcal{H}$. Hence there exists an element
$w \in \mathcal{H}$ such that $L(x) = (x, w)$. It is obvious that
$\int (x(p), w'(p) - w(p)) dr(p) = 0$ for all $x \in \mathcal{H}$. Putting $x = Sy$ with
$S \in \mathcal{C}$ and recalling that $(Sy)(p) = S(p) y(p)$ a.e., there results the
equation $\int S(p) (y(p), w'(p) - w(p)) = 0$. As S ranges over $\mathcal{C}$, $S(.)$
ranges over the space of all bounded measurable functions on M, and it
follows that $(y(p), w'(p) - w(p)) = 0$ a.e., or $(w'(p), y(p)) =$
$(w(p), y(p))$ a.e., i.e., condition 2b) in the definition of a direct
integral of Hilbert spaces is valid. If Q is separable, say with
$\{U_i;\; i=1,2,\ldots,\}$ dense, then the $\eta_p(U_i)$ are dense in $\mathcal{H}_p$, and as

$(w'(p), \eta_p(U_1)) = (w(p), \eta_p(U_1))$ simultaneously for all i, a.e., it results that $w'(p) = w(p)$ a.e. so that the integral is strong.

It remains to show that if an operator T is decomposable or diagonalizable, then it is, respectively, in C' or C. Now suppose that T is decomposable, so that $(Tx, y) = \int (T(p) x(p), y(p))\, dr(p)$ for all x and y in $\mathcal{H}$, and some function $T(p)$ such that $T(p)$ is an operator on H_p for $p \in R$, and with $\| T(p) \|$ essentially bounded on M. If S is arbitrary in C, we have $(TSx, y) = \int (T(p)(Sx)(p), y(p))\, dr(p) = \int (T(p)S(p)x(p), y(p))\, dr(p) = \int (T(p)x(p), S(p)y(p))\, dr(p) =$

$$\int (T(p)x(p), (S*y)(p))\, dr(p) = (Tx, S*y) = (STx, y).$$

Hence $ST = TS$ or $T \in C'$. It is trivial to show from the fact that C is isomorphic with the algebra of all bounded measurable functions on M, that a diagonalizable operator must be in C.

The proof of Theorem 2 is thereby concluded, and we have incidentally established the following corollaries.

COROLLARY 2.1. If $S \in C$, $T \in \mathcal{Q}$, $x \in \mathcal{H}$, and if $x(p)$ is the decomposition of x, then the decomposition of Sx is $S(p)x(p)$ and the decomposition of Tx is $\varphi_p(T)x(p)$.

COROLLARY 2.2. If $x_i \in \mathcal{H}$ $(i = 1, 2, \ldots)$ and $x_i \longrightarrow x$, then there exists a subsequence $\{n_i\}$ of the positive integers such that $x_{n_i}(p) \longrightarrow x(p)$ a.e.

We close this section by obtaining a result which will be useful in the treatment of separable Hilbert spaces.

THEOREM 3. With the notation of Theorem 2, let $\mathcal{Q}$ be separable (in the uniform topology). Then every strong limit of a sequence of operators in $\mathcal{Q}$ is decomposable relative to the decomposition of $\mathcal{H}$ described in Theorem 2.

I. E. Segal

Let $\{T_n\}$ be a sequence of operators on Q which converges strongly to an operator T; it must be shown that T is decomposable. Let $\{U_i\}$ be a countable dense subset of Q, and set $x_i = U_i z$; then $\{x_i\}$ is dense in $\mathcal{H}$. By Corollary 2.2, there exists a subsequence $\{n_{1,1}\}$ of the integers such that $T_{n_{1,1}}(p)\, x_1(p)$ converges a.e. to $(Tx_1)(p)$. Next, there exists a subsequence $\{n_{1,2}\}$ of the $n_{1,1}$ such that $T_{n_{1,2}}(p)x_2(p)$ converges a.e. to $(Tx_2)(p)$. Proceeding in this fashion by induction, and employing the Cantor diagonal process, it follows that there exists a subsequence $\{n_i\}$ of the integers such that $T_{n_i}(p)x_j(p)$ converges a.e. as $i \longrightarrow \infty$ to $(Tx_j)(p)$. Now as the U_j are dense in Q, the $\eta_p(U_j)$ are, for each $p \in R$, dense in $\mathcal{H}_p$. Moreover, $\|T_n\|$ is bounded because $\{T_n\}$ is strongly convergent, and hence $\|T_{n_i}(p)\|$ is bounded for $p \in R$ and $i = 1, 2, \ldots$. A bounded sequence of operators which converge on a dense set is strongly convergent, and hence $\{T_{n_i}(p)\}$ has a.e. a strong limit $T(p)$.

It is clear that $T(p)\, x_j(p) = (Tx_j)(p)$ a.e. It follows easily that $(Tx, y) = \int (T(p)\, x(p),\, y(p))\, dr(p)$ in the special case in which x is one of the x_j and y is arbitrary in $\mathcal{H}$. Now if x is arbitrary in $\mathcal{H}$ and if $\{x_j'\}$ is a subsequence of the x_j such that $x_j' \longrightarrow x$, then clearly $(Tx_j', y) \longrightarrow (Tx, y)$ and on the other hand $\int \| x_j'(p) - x(p) \|^2\, dr(p) \longrightarrow 0$. Now $\| T(p) \| \leq \limsup_i \| T_{n_i}(p) \| \leq \| T \|$, so that (noting that $(T(p)\, x(p),\, y(p))$ is measurable on M, being a.e. equal to $\lim_i (T_{n_i}(p)\, x(p),\, y(p))$)

$$\left| \int (T(p)\, x_j'(p),\, y(p))\, dr(p) - \int (T(p)\, x(p),\, y(p))\, dr(p) \right| \leq$$

$$\int |(T(p)\, x_j'(p) - x(p),\, y(p))|\, dr(p) \leq \int \| T \|\ \| x_j'(p) - x(p) \|\ \| y(p) \|\, dr(p)$$

$\leq \| T \| \, \| x_j' - x \| \, \| y \| \longrightarrow 0$. It follows that the preceding equation for (Tx, y) holds for arbitrary x and y in $\mathcal{H}$.

$\underline{\text{Definition 4.2}}$. If T is the strong limit of a sequence $\{T_n\}$ in $\mathcal{Q}$ such that $\{T_n(p) \equiv \varphi_p(T_n)\}$ converges strongly for almost all $p \in R$ to $T(p)$, then $T(\cdot)$ is called the $\underline{\text{canonical decomposition}}$ of T (with respect to $\mathcal{Q}$, $\mathcal{C}$, and z).

$\underline{\text{Remark 4.1}}$. To justify the preceding definition it should be shown that the canonical decomposition of T is unique. Suppose now that $\{T_n'\}$ is a sequence in $\mathcal{Q}$ which converges strongly to T and that a.e. on M, $T_n'(p)$ converges strongly to $T'(p)$. Then a.e., for all U_1 in the dense subset of $\mathcal{Q}$ which occurs in the proof of the preceding theorem, $\| T_n(p) \, \eta_p(U_1) - T(p) \, \eta_p(U_1) \| \longrightarrow 0$, and $\| T_n'(p) \, \eta_p(U_1) - T'(p) \, \eta_p(U_1) \| \longrightarrow 0$. Now $\| (T_n - T_n')U_1 z \|^2 = \int \| (T_n(p) - T_n'(p)) \, \eta_p(U_1) \|^2 \, dr(p)$, and so there exists a subsequence $\{n_j\}$ of the integers such that $\| T_{n_j}(p) \, \eta_p(U_1) - T_{n_j}' \, \eta_p(U_1) \| \longrightarrow 0$ as

$j \longrightarrow \infty$, a.e. simultaneously in 1. By Minkowski's inequality, $\| T(p) \, \eta_p(U_1) - T'(p) \, \eta_p(U_1) \| \leq \| T(p) \, \eta_p(U_1) - T_{n_j}(p) \, \eta_p(U_1) \| + \| T_{n_j}(p) \, \eta_p(U_1) - T_{n_j}'(p) \, \eta_p(U_1) \| + \| T_{n_j}'(p) \, \eta_p(U_1) - T'(p) \, \eta_p(U_1) \|$ and it results that $\| T(p) \, \eta_p(U_1) - T'(p) \, \eta_p(U_1) \| = 0$ a.e. simultaneously in 1. As for each $p \in R$, the $\eta_p(U_1)$ are dense in $\mathcal{H}_p$, it follows that a.e. $T(p) = T'(p)$.

COROLLARY 3.1. $\underline{\text{If } T \text{ and } U \text{ are strong limits of sequences in}}$ $\mathcal{Q}$, $\underline{\text{if } x \in \mathcal{H}, \text{ and if } \alpha \text{ is a complex number, then the following equa-}}$ $\underline{\text{tions hold a.e.}}$: $(T + U)(p) = T(p) + U(p)$; $(TU)(p) = T(p)U(p)$; $(\alpha T)(p) = \alpha T(p)$; $(Tx)(p) = T(p)x(p)$. $\underline{\text{Here } T(\cdot) \text{ and } U(\cdot) \text{ are the}}$ $\underline{\text{canonical decompositions of } T \text{ and } U \text{ and } x(\cdot) \text{ and } (Tx)(\cdot) \text{ are the}}$

<u>decompositions</u> <u>of</u> x <u>and</u> Tx, <u>respectively.</u>

Let $\{T_n\}$ and $\{U_n\}$ be sequences in Q which converge to T and U respectively, and such that $\{T_n(p)\}$ and $\{U_n(p)\}$ a.e. converge to $T(p)$ and $U(p)$ respectively. Then $\{T_n + U_n\}$ converges strongly to $T + U$, and a.e. $\{T_n(p) + U_n(p)\}$ converges strongly to $T(p) + U(p)$, which shows that $(T + U)(p) = T(p) + U(p)$ (a.e.). Similarly, it follows that $(TU)(p) = T(p)U(p)$ and $(\alpha T)(p) = \alpha T(p)$.

If x is arbitrary in $\mathcal{H}$, $\|(Tx)(p) - T(p)x(p)\|$ is a.e. equal to $\lim_n \|(Tx)(p) - T_n(p)x(p)\|$. On the other hand, $\int \|(Tx)(p) - T_n(p)x(p)\|^2 dr(p) = \|Tx - T_nx\|^2 \longrightarrow 0$, and so by Corollary 2.2 there exists a subsequence $\{n_i\}$ of the integers such that $\|(Tx)(p) - T_{n_1}(p)x(p)\| \longrightarrow 0$ a.e. It follows that $\|(Tx)(p) - T_{n_1}(p)x(p)\| = 0$ a.e., i.e., $(Tx)(p) = T(p)x(p)$ a.e.

Remark 4.3. A slight modification of the proof of Theorem 3 shows that every strong limit of a sequence of decomposable operators is itself decomposable. For as Q is separable, Q_z is separable, so that $\mathcal{H}$ is separable. If $\{x_i;\ i = 1,\ 2,\ \ldots\}$ is a countable dense subset of $\mathcal{H}$, then $\{x_i(\gamma);\ i = 1,\ 2,\ \ldots\}$ is a.e. dense in $\mathcal{H}_\gamma$, for by Corollary 2.2, if $\{x_{ij}\}$ is a subsequence of $\{x_i\}$ which converges to $U_j z$, there is a subsequence of this subsequence whose decomposition function converges a.e. to $\eta_\gamma(U_j)$, and the $\eta_\gamma(U_j)$ are dense in $\mathcal{H}_\gamma$. The remainder of the proof is the same. We note finally that as a weak limit of a sequence of operators is a strong limit of a sequence of finite linear combinations of the operators (cf. [18]), the set of all decomposable operators is closed in the weak sequential topology, when Q is separable.

5. <u>Maximal decompositions.</u> The complete reduction of an algebra of linear transformations on a finite-dimensional linear space is determined by the selection of a maximal Boolean algebra of invariant subspaces under

the algebra. Such a selection is likewise possible in the case of Hilbert space. In fact, it is not difficult to show that if $\mathcal{Q}$ is a C*-algebra on a Hilbert space $\mathcal{H}$, and if $\mathcal{C}$ is any maximal abelian self-adjoint subalgebra of $\mathcal{Q}'$, then the ranges of the projections in $\mathcal{C}$ constitute a maximal Boolean algebra of closed invariant subspaces under $\mathcal{Q}$. (Actually, the Zorn principle shows that such a selection is possible on any linear space, but in the case of Hilbert space, it can be made in the foregoing way, with complementation in the Boolean algebra coinciding with orthogonal complementation.) The main purpose of this section is to show that if $\mathcal{Q}$ is separable, then the components in the reduction of $\mathcal{Q}$ relative to such an algebra $\mathcal{C}$ as in the preceding sections, are a.e. irreducible. That is, the $\mathcal{H}_p$ are a.e. irreducible under the $\varphi_p(\mathcal{Q})$. A similar result, based on the von Neumann reduction theory, is due to Mautner [6]. In the next section we apply our result here to obtain a decomposition into factors of an arbitrary W*-algebra, similar to that obtained by von Neumann, for "rings" with respect to their centers.

THEOREM 4. With the notations of Theorems 1 and 2, let the state decomposition hypothesized in Theorem 2 be that obtained in Theorem 1, so $M = (\Gamma, \mu)$ and let $\mathcal{C}$ be maximal abelian in $\mathcal{Q}'$. Then φ_γ is almost everywhere irreducible.

We first prove a lemma on inverses of continuous maps of compact spaces which plays a role somewhat similar to that of a lemma of von Neumann [16, Lemma 5] concerning inverses of continuous functions on analytic sets.

LEMMA 4.1. Let f be a continuous function from a compact metric space C to a compact metric space D. If E is an open subset of C, there exists a Borel function g on $f(E)$ to C, such that $g(y) \in f^{-1}(y) \cap E$ for $y \in f(E)$.

We shall present the proof in stages, first considering the case $E = C$, then the case in which E is closed rather than open, and finally the general case. This arrangement of the proof is not logically necessary, but seems to clarify its structure.

SUBLEMMA 4.1.1. <u>The Lemma is valid in case</u> $E = C$.

Let $\{x_n\}$ be a countable dense set in C such that $x_n \neq x_m$ if $n \neq m$ ($n = 1, 2, \ldots$) (we shall assume that C is not finite, as the result is obvious for the finite case). Let $S_e(x)$ denote the set of all points $x' \in C$ such that $d(x, x') < e$, where $d(x, x')$ denotes the distance from x to x', and $e > 0$. We define a function $g_1(y)$ on D as follows: $g_1(y) =$ that x_n which has the least index n among the m such that $S_1(x_m) \# f^{-1}(y)$, where $A \# B$ means that the sets A and B intersect. It is clear that such points x_m exist, for otherwise there would exist points in C whose distance from the x_m was ≥ 1. Now g_1 is a Borel function. To show this it suffices, in view of the circumstance that g_1 is (at most) countably-valued with values among the x_n, to show that for any n, $g_1^{-1}(x_n)$ is a Borel set. Clearly $g_1^{-1}(x_n)$ is the set of all y such that a) $S_1(x_n)\#f^{-1}(y)$, and b) n is the least m such that $S_1(x_m)\#f^{-1}(y)$. Since the assertion $S_1(x_m)\#f^{-1}(y)$ is equivalent to the assertion $y \in f(S_1(x_m))$, it follows that $g_1^{-1}(x_n) = f(S_1(x_n)) - \bigcup_{p<n} f(S_1(x_p))$. Now $S_e(x)$ is a countable union of closed subsets, and hence a countable union of compact subsets. By the compactness of a continuous image of a compact set, $f(S_e(x))$ is a countable union of compact sets, and so is a Borel set. It results that $g_1^{-1}(x_n)$ is Borel.

Next we define $g_2(y)$ as that x_n which has the least index m among m for which $S_{1/2}(x_m)\#f^{-1}(y) \cap S_1(g_1(y))$. By the same argument as before, $g_2(y)$ exists, and its values are among the x_n. Now $g_2^{-1}(x_n) =$

$[y \mid g_2(y) = x_n] = \bigcup_m [y \mid g_2(y) = x_n, \ g_1(y) = x_m] =$
$\bigcup_m [y \mid n$ is least p such that $S_{1/2}(x_p) \cap f^{-1}(y) \cap S_1(x_m) \neq 0] \cap$
$[y \mid g_1(y) = x_m]$. Since g_1 is Borel, so is $[y \mid g_1(y) = x_m]$. Moreover,
$[y \mid n$ is least p such that $S_{1/2}(x_p) \cap f^{-1}(y) \cap S_1(x_m) \neq 0] =$
$[y \mid n$ is least p such that $y \in f(S_{1/2}(x_p) \cap S_1(x_m))] =$
$f(S_{1/2}(x_n) \cap S_1(x_n)) - \bigcup_{p < n} f(S_{1/2}(x_p) \cap S_1(x_m))$, which is easily seen

to be Borel. We note also that $d(g_1(y), g_2(y)) < 3/2$, for if $g_2(y) = x_n$,
then $S_{1/2}(x_n) \# S_1(g_1(y))$.

Now we define g_r by induction as follows: $g_r(y)$ is that
x_n which has the least index p such that
$$S_{1/2^{r-1}}(x_p) \ \# \ (f^{-1}(y) \cap S_{1/2^{r-2}}(g_{r-1}(y))).$$
Then clearly $g_r^{-1}(x_n) = [y \mid g_r(y) = x_n] = \bigcup_m [y \mid n$ is least p such that

$S_{1/2^{r-1}}(x_p) \# (f^{-1}(y) \cap S_{1/2^{r-2}}(x_m)] \cap [y \mid g_{r-1}(y) = x_m]$. Now

$[y \mid g_{r-1}(y) = x_n]$ is Borel by the induction hypothesis, and the other set
involved in the intersection behind $\bigcup_m$ is $[y \mid n$ is least p such that
$y \in f(S_{1/2^{r-1}}(x_p) \cap S_{1/2^{r-2}}(x_m)] = f(S_{1/2^{r-1}}(x_n) \cap S_{1/2^{r-2}}(x_m)) -$
$\bigcup_{p < n} f(S_{1/2^{r-1}}(x_p) \cap S_{1/2^{r-2}}(x_n))$, which is Borel. Thus $g_r^{-1}(x_n)$ is

Borel, and hence so is g_r. Finally, $d(g_r(y), g_{r-1}(y)) < (1/2^{r-1}) +$
$(1/2^{r-2})$, since a sphere of radius $1/2^{r-1}$ around $g_r(y)$ meets a sphere
of radius $1/2^{r-2}$ around $g_{r-1}(y)$.

Clearly the series $\sum_{r=1}^{\infty} d(g_{r+1}(y), g_r(y))$ is convergent, and

hence the sequence $\{g_n(y)\}$ converges uniformly to a Borel function g.
Now $g_n(y)$ is of distance less than $1/2^{n-1}$ from the closed set $f^{-1}(y)$,
and hence $g(y) \in f^{-1}(y)$, concluding the proof of the sublemma.

I. E. Segal

SUBLEMMA 4.1.2. With the notation of Lemma 4.1, let G be a closed subset of C, and let g_o be a Borel function on $F = f(G)$ to G such that $g_o(y) \in f^{-1}(y)$, for $y \in F$. Then there exists a Borel function g on D to C which coincides on F with g_o, and such that $g(y) \in f^{-1}(y)$ for $y \in D$.

Let $\{x_n\}$ be dense in $C - G$ (which we may assume to be infinite). We define a function g_1 on D as follows: $g_1(y) = g_o(y)$ if $y \in F$, and if $y \notin F$, then $g_1(y)$ is that x_n such that n is the least p for which $S_1(x_p) \# f^{-1}(y)$. Then g_1 is Borel, for if K is any closed set in C, $g_1^{-1}(K) = g_1^{-1}(K \cap G) \cup g_1^{-1}(K - G)$. Now $g_1^{-1}(K \cap G) = g_o^{-1}(K \cap G)$, which is a Borel subset of F and hence a Borel subset of D. To show that $g_1^{-1}(K - G)$ is Borel, it suffices to show that $g_1^{-1}(x_n)$ is Borel, and this can be done just as in the proof of the first sublemma. The proof may now be completed by constructing a sequence $\{g_n\}$ by induction, again just as in the proof of Sublemma 1.

PROOF OF LEMMA. Let $E = \bigcup_n G_n$, where $G_{n+1} \supset G_n$ and the G_n are compact, and let $F_n = f(G_n)$. By Sublemma 2 and induction there exists a sequence $\{h_n\}$ of Borel functions h_n on F_n to G_n such that $h_n^{-1}(y) \in f^{-1}(y)$ and h_{n+1} agrees with h_n on F_n. Let z be an arbitrary fixed point in C, and define g_n on $f(E)$ by setting $g_n(y) = h_n(y)$ for $y \in F_n$, and $g_n(y) = z$ for $y \notin F_n$. Then it is easily seen that g_n is Borel. Now for any fixed $y \in f(E)$, $y \in F_n$ for sufficiently large n, so that $g_n(y)$ converges, say to $g(y)$, with $g(y) \in f^{-1}(y)$. It is plain that g is a function satisfying the conclusion of the lemma.

The following lemma shows roughly that the φ_γ are irreducible "on the average".

LEMMA 4.2. With the notation of the present theorem, suppose that $\omega_\gamma = \alpha(\gamma)\rho_\gamma + \beta(\gamma)\sigma_\gamma$, where $\alpha(\gamma)$ and $\beta(\gamma)$ are measurable functions on Γ to the interval $(0, 1)$ such that $\alpha(\gamma) + \beta(\gamma) = 1$ for all γ, and where for each $U \in \mathcal{Q}$, $\rho_\gamma(U)$ and $\sigma_\gamma(U)$ are measurable functions of γ, ρ_γ and σ_γ being in the conjugate space of $\mathcal{Q}$ and a.e. states of $\mathcal{Q}$. Then a.e. $\rho_\gamma = \omega_\gamma$.

If $\alpha(\gamma) \leq 1/2$ we put $\rho'_\gamma = 2(\alpha(\gamma)\rho_\gamma + (\beta(\gamma) - 1/2)\sigma_\gamma)$ and $\sigma'_\gamma = \sigma_\gamma$; if $\alpha(\gamma) > 1/2$ we put $\rho'_\gamma = \rho_\gamma$ and $\sigma'_\gamma = 2(\alpha(\gamma) - 1/2)\rho_\gamma + \beta(\gamma)\sigma_\gamma)$. Then $\omega_\gamma = (1/2)(\rho'_\gamma + \sigma'_\gamma)$, $\rho'_\gamma(U)$ and $\sigma'_\gamma(U)$ are measurable functions of γ for $U \in \mathcal{Q}$, and ρ'_γ and σ'_γ are states a.e. Hence it suffices to consider the case in which $\alpha(\gamma) = \beta(\gamma) = 1/2$.

As proved in [8, page 80] (though not stated formally as a theorem) the equation $2\omega_\gamma = \rho_\gamma + \sigma_\gamma$ implies that $\rho_\gamma(U) = (T_\gamma \varphi_\gamma(U)z_\gamma, z_\gamma)$ for $U \in \mathcal{Q}$, where $T_\gamma \in (\varphi_\gamma(\mathcal{Q}))'$ and $\| T_\gamma \| \leq 2$. Now if U and V are in $\mathcal{Q}$, $(T_\gamma \eta_\gamma(U), \eta_\gamma(V)) = (T_\gamma \varphi_\gamma(U)z_\gamma, \varphi_\gamma(V)z_\gamma) = (T_\gamma \varphi_\gamma(V*U)z_\gamma, z_\gamma) = \rho_\gamma(V*U)$, and so is a measurable function of γ. It follows readily that for arbitrary x and y in $\mathcal{H}$, $(T_\gamma x(\gamma), y(\gamma))$ is a measurable function of γ. Hence there exists an operator T on $\mathcal{H}$ such that $(Tx, y) = \int (T_\gamma x(\gamma), y(\gamma)) d\mu(\gamma)$ for all x and y in $\mathcal{H}$.

As T is decomposable, $T \in C'$. On the other hand, $T \in \mathcal{Q}'$, for if U, V, and W are in $\mathcal{Q}$, $(TUVz, Wz) = \int (T_\gamma \eta_\gamma(UV), \eta_\gamma(W)) d\mu(\gamma) = \int (T_\gamma \varphi_\gamma(U) \eta_\gamma(V), \eta_\gamma(W)) d\mu(\gamma) = \int (\varphi_\gamma(U)T_\gamma \eta_\gamma(V), \eta_\gamma(W)) d\mu(\gamma) = \int (T_\gamma \eta_\gamma(V), \varphi_\gamma(U*) \eta_\gamma(W)) d\mu(\gamma) = \int (T_\gamma \eta_\gamma(V), \eta_\gamma(U*W)) d\mu(\gamma) = (TVz, U*Wz) = (UTVz, Wz)$. As V and W range over $\mathcal{Q}$, Vz and Wz range over dense subsets of $\mathcal{H}$, and from this it follows that $(TUx, y) = (UTx, y)$ for all x and y in $\mathcal{H}$, so that $TU = UT$.

Thus $T \in \mathcal{Q}' \cap C'$, but by assumption, $\mathcal{Q}' \cap C' = C$. Now let $T(\gamma)$ be the continuous function on Γ corresponding to T and let S be arbitrary in C. Then $(STx, y) = (Tx, S*y) = \int (T_\gamma x(\gamma), S(\gamma)y(\gamma)) d\mu(\gamma)$ (by Corollary 2.1) $= \int S(\gamma)(T_\gamma x(\gamma), y(\gamma)) d\mu(\gamma)$. On the other hand, $(STx, y) = \int S(\gamma) T(\gamma)(x(\gamma), y(\gamma)) \, d\mu(\gamma)$. From the arbitrary character of S it results that $(T_\gamma x(\gamma), y(\gamma)) = T(\gamma)(x(\gamma), y(\gamma))$ a.e. In particular $(T_\gamma \eta_\gamma(U), \eta_\gamma(V)) = T(\gamma) (\eta_\gamma(U), \eta_\gamma(V))$ a.e. if U and V are in $\mathcal{A}$, and if $\{U_i\}$ is any sequence of elements of $\mathcal{A}$, $(T_\gamma \eta_\gamma(U_i), \eta_\gamma(U_j)) = T(\gamma) (\eta_\gamma(U_i), \eta_\gamma(U_j))$ holds simultaneously for all i and j a.e. Now assuming the U_i to constitute a dense subset of $\mathcal{A}$, the $\eta_\gamma(U_i)$ are dense in $\mathcal{H}_\gamma$, and hence a.e. $(T_\gamma x_\gamma, y_\gamma) = T(\gamma) (x_\gamma, y_\gamma)$ for all x_γ and y_γ in $\mathcal{H}_\gamma$. Therefore $T_\gamma = T(\gamma)$ a.e. so that a.e. ρ_γ is proportional to ω_γ, and as ρ_γ and ω_γ are both states, $\omega_\gamma = \rho_\gamma$ a.e.

PROOF OF THEOREM. Let N be a Borel set of measure zero which contains the set of γ's for which ω_γ is not a state. Let Ω be the state space of the C*-algebra $\mathcal{A}_1$ generated by $\mathcal{A}$ and the identity I. Then $\mathcal{A}_1$ consists of all operators of the form $\alpha I + U$, with $U \in \mathcal{A}$, and so is separable. It follows that Ω is compact metric (if $\{U_i\}$ is a dense sequence in $\mathcal{A}_1$, $d(\rho, \sigma) = \sum_i 2^{-1} \| U_i \|^{-1} |\rho(U_i) - \sigma(U_i)|$ is a metric inducing the weak topology). For any state ω of $\mathcal{A}$, let ω' denote the extension to $\mathcal{A}_1$ defined by the equation $\omega'(\alpha I + U) = \alpha + \omega(U)$; then ω' is a state of $\mathcal{A}_1$ and is pure if and only if ω is pure. That ω' is a state is clear with the exception of the requirement that $\omega'(\alpha I + U) \geq 0$ if $\alpha I + U \geq 0$. Now $\alpha I + U \geq 0$ means $\alpha I + U = (\beta I + V)^2$ with $V \in \mathcal{A}$ and $\beta I + V$ self-adjoint. We can suppose that β is real and $V = V*$, for otherwise the equation $\beta I + V = (\beta I + V)*$ implies that $I = (\bar{\beta} - \beta)(V - V*)$ so that $I \in \mathcal{A}$ and $\mathcal{A}_1 = \mathcal{A}$. Plainly $\omega'(\beta I + V) = \beta^2 + 2\beta\omega(V) + \omega(V^2)$, which is non-negative for real β by the fact that the geometric mean is dominated by the arithmetic mean. It is immediate that ω is pure if ω' is pure, and the converse is proved in [8], p. 87.

Now let C be the product space $\Omega \times \Omega$, D the space Ω, f the mapping $(\rho', \sigma') \longrightarrow (1/2)(\rho' + \sigma')$, and E the subset of C consisting of all elements of the form (ρ', σ') with $\rho' \neq \sigma'$. Now C - E is the diagonal set of all (ρ', ρ') with $\rho' \in \Omega$; as Ω is compact and the mapping $\rho' \longrightarrow (\rho', \rho')$ continuous, C - E is compact and hence E is open. It follows that Lemma 4.1 applies and states that there exists a Borel mapping ψ on the set Ω_o of non-extreme points of Ω to $\Omega \times \Omega$ such that if $\psi(\omega') = (\rho', \sigma')$, then $\omega' = (1/2)(\rho' + \sigma')$. For an extreme point ω' of Ω we extend ψ by defining $\psi(\omega') = \omega$; ψ is then defined on Ω, and is Borel. To show that ψ is Borel actually, let K be any closed subset of $\Omega \times \Omega$ and K_1 the set of all elements of K which are diagonal. Then $\psi^{-1}(K) = \psi^{-1}(K_1) \cup \psi^{-1}(K - K_1)$. Now $K_1 = K \cap (C - E)$ and hence is compact; as $\rho' \longrightarrow (\rho', \rho')$ is a homeomorphism on Ω to C - E, and as ψ^{-1} on C - E takes (ρ', ρ') into ρ', $\psi^{-1}(K_1)$ is compact and hence Borel in Ω. Now $K - K_1$ is the intersection of E with a closed set and so is closed relative to E; as ψ before extension was Borel, $\psi^{-1}(K - K_1)$ must be Borel. Finally $\psi^{-1}(K)$ is Borel, being the union of two Borel sets.

We put $\psi(\omega') = (\xi(\omega'), \chi(\omega'))$, and then ξ and χ are likewise Borel, being compositions of Borel with continuous functions. Let J be the mapping $\omega' \longrightarrow \omega$ of states of $\mathcal{Q}_1$ into the continuous linear functionals on $\mathcal{Q}$; then it is clear from the definition of the weak topology that J is continuous. Now let $\rho_\gamma = J\xi(\omega'_\gamma)$ and $\sigma_\gamma = J\chi(\omega'_\gamma)$ for $\gamma \notin N$, so that ρ_γ and σ_γ are states of $\mathcal{Q}$ when ω_γ is a state, and $(1/2)(\rho_\gamma + \sigma_\gamma) = \omega_\gamma$. For any $U \in \mathcal{Q}$, $\rho_\gamma(U)$ and $\sigma_\gamma(U)$ are measurable functions on $\Gamma - N$, for taking the case of $\rho_\gamma(U)$, it is the product of the successive maps (a) $\gamma \longrightarrow \omega_\gamma$, on $\Gamma - N$ to the state space of $\mathcal{Q}$; (b) $\omega \longrightarrow \omega'$ on the state space of $\mathcal{Q}$ to Ω; (c) $\omega' \longrightarrow \xi(\omega')$ on Ω to Ω; (d) $\omega' \longrightarrow J\omega$, on Ω to the state space of A; (e) $\omega \longrightarrow \omega(U)$ on the state space of Q to the complex numbers. Now (c) is a Borel map, (b) is easily seen to be continuous, and the other maps are obviously continuous. Therefore, if G is any closed set of complex numbers, $[\gamma \mid \rho_\gamma(U) \in G, \gamma \notin N]$ is a Borel subset of $\Gamma - N$, and as N is a Borel set, a Borel subset of Γ. Hence Lemma 4.2 applies and shows that $\rho_\gamma = \omega_\gamma$ a.e. It follows that ω_γ is extreme, i.e. pure, a.e., so that by [8] φ_γ is irreducible.

PART II. APPLICATIONS

6. <u>Decomposition of a W*-algebra into factors</u>. We show in this section that any W*-algebra with an identity (= ring in the sense of von Neumann) on a separable Hilbert space can be decomposed into a kind of direct integral of factors. A similar decomposition of a W*-algebra into more elementary W*-algebras is valid also for inseparable spaces, but we are not then able to assert that these elementary algebras are factors. We begin by stating just what is meant by such a decomposition.

<u>Definition 6.1</u>. Let the Hilbert space $\mathcal{H}$ be the direct integral of the Hilbert spaces $\mathcal{H}_p$, as in Definition 4.1. An algebra Q of operators on $\mathcal{H}$ is said to be the <u>direct integral</u> of algebras Q_p of operators on $\mathcal{H}_p$, with respect to the given decomposition of $\mathcal{H}$ as a direct integral, if: a) every $T \in Q$ has a decomposition $T(p)$ with $T(p) \in Q_p$ a.e.; b) every decomposable operator T on $\mathcal{H}$ such that $T(p) \in Q_p$ a.e. is in Q. We then write symbolically $Q = \int Q_p \, dr(p)$.

THEOREM 5. <u>Let</u> Q <u>be a weakly closed self-adjoint algebra of operators on a Hilbert space</u> $\mathcal{H}$, <u>which contains the identity and has center</u> C. <u>Then</u> Q <u>is a direct integral of factors, relative to a decomposition of</u> $\mathcal{H}$ <u>as a strong direct integral whose algebra of diagonalizable operators is</u> C.

LEMMA. $\mathcal{Q}$ <u>contains a</u> C*-<u>subalgebra</u> $\mathcal{D}$ <u>which is separable (in the uniform topology), whose strong sequential closure is</u> $\mathcal{Q}$, <u>and which contains the identity operator</u>.

This lemma follows at once from von Neumann's theorem that $\mathcal{Q}$ contains a countable subset dense in the strong sequential topology [17 , p. 386.]

PROOF OF THEOREM. Let $\mathcal{D}$ and $\mathcal{E}$ be separable C*-algebras containing I which are dense in $\mathcal{Q}$ and $\mathcal{Q}'$ respectively, in the strong sequential topology, and let $\mathcal{F}$ be the C*-algebra generated by $\mathcal{D}$ and $\mathcal{E}$. Then $\mathcal{F}$ is separable, for rational linear combinations of monomials in the elements of a dense subset of $\mathcal{D}$ and a dense subset of $\mathcal{E}$ yield a countable dense subset of $\mathcal{F}$. It is not difficult to see that $\mathcal{D}' = \mathcal{Q}'$, that $\mathcal{E}' = \mathcal{Q}'' = \mathcal{Q}$ (by a well-known theorem of von Neumann), and that $\mathcal{F}' = \mathcal{D}' \cap \mathcal{E}' = \mathcal{Q}' \cap \mathcal{Q} = \mathcal{C}$. As $\mathcal{C}$ is abelian, $\mathcal{C}'$ contains every self-adjoint maximal abelian subalgebra of $\mathcal{B}$ which contains $\mathcal{C}$. Now such a maximal abelian subalgebra is known to have a cyclic element, say z, which we can take to be normalized. A fortiori, $\mathcal{C}'z$ is dense in $\mathcal{H}$. Now $\mathcal{F}'' = \mathcal{C}'$ clearly, but $\mathcal{F}''$ is the strong closure of $\mathcal{F}$, by the theorem of von Neumann just cited. Thus $\mathcal{F}$ is strongly dense in $\mathcal{C}'$ and it follows that $\mathcal{F}z$ is dense in $\mathcal{H}$.

We are now in a position to apply Theorems 2 and 3 with $\mathcal{Q}$ replaced by $\mathcal{F}$. Let $\mathcal{Q}_\gamma$ be the strong closure of $\varphi_\gamma(\mathcal{D})$. If $T \in \mathcal{Q}$, then T is the strong limit of a sequence $\{T_n\}$ in $\mathcal{D}$, but $\mathcal{D} \subset \mathcal{F}$, so that T is decomposable by Theorem 3. Putting $T(\gamma)$ for its canonical decomposition, so that a.e. $T(\gamma) = $ strong $\lim_n T_n(\gamma)$ if the sequence $\{T_n\}$ is suitably chosen in $\mathcal{D}$, then for almost all γ , $T(\gamma)$ is the strong limit of a sequence in $\mathcal{Q}_\gamma$, and hence is itself in $\mathcal{Q}_\gamma$. On the other hand, if T is a decomposable operator with decomposition $T(.)$ such that a.e. $T(\gamma) \in \mathcal{Q}_\gamma$, so that $(Tx, y) = \int (T(\gamma)x(\gamma), y(\gamma))\, d\mu(\gamma)$ for all x

and y in $\mathcal{H}$, we shall show that $T \in \mathcal{Q}$. If $U \in \mathcal{Q}'$, then by the argument just made U is decomposable with a canonical decomposition U(.)
such that $U(\gamma)$ is a.e. in the strong closure of $\varphi_\gamma(\mathcal{E})$. By Corollary
3.1, UT and TU are both decomposable, with decompositions U(.)T(.)
and T(.)U(.) respectively. As each element of $\mathcal{D}$ commutes with each
element of $\mathcal{E}$, each element of $\varphi_\gamma(\mathcal{D})$ also commutes with each element
of $\varphi_\gamma(\mathcal{E})$. It follows easily (using the identity of the strong and weak
closures of SA algebras) that each element of the strong closure of
$\varphi_\gamma(\mathcal{D})$ commutes with each element of the strong closure of $\varphi_\gamma(\mathcal{E})$. In
particular, a.e. $U(\gamma)$ and $T(\gamma)$ commute. It results that UT = TU,
or $T \in \mathcal{Q}''$, i.e., $T \in \mathcal{Q}$.

Thus $\mathcal{Q}$ is the direct integral of the $\mathcal{Q}_\gamma$. It remains to show
that a.e. $\mathcal{Q}_\gamma$ is a factor. By Theorem 4, $\mathcal{H}_\gamma$ is a.e. irreducible under
$\varphi_\gamma(\mathcal{F})$. An equivalent way of stating this is as follows: $(\varphi_\gamma(\mathcal{F}))' =$
$\mathcal{S}_\gamma$ a.e., where $\mathcal{S}_\gamma$ is the algebra of all scalar operators on $\mathcal{H}_\gamma$. Now
$\mathcal{F}$ is generated as a C*-algebra by $\mathcal{D}$ and $\mathcal{E}$, and it follows readily
that $\varphi_\gamma(\mathcal{F})$ is likewise so generated by $\varphi_\gamma(\mathcal{D})$ and $\varphi_\gamma(\mathcal{E})$. It
follows that $(\varphi_\gamma(\mathcal{F}))' = (\varphi_\gamma(\mathcal{D}))' \cap (\varphi_\gamma(\mathcal{E}))'$. Putting $\mathcal{M}_\gamma$ for the
strong closure of $\varphi_\gamma(\mathcal{E})$, as noted earlier $(\mathcal{Q}_\gamma)' = (\varphi_\gamma(\mathcal{D}))'$, so
$(\mathcal{Q}_\gamma)' \cap (\mathcal{M}_\gamma)' = \mathcal{S}_\gamma$ a.e. Now each element of $\mathcal{Q}_\gamma$ commutes with each
element of $\mathcal{M}_\gamma$, i.e., $(\mathcal{M}_\gamma)' \supset \mathcal{Q}_\gamma$, so $(\mathcal{Q}_\gamma)' \cap \mathcal{Q}_\gamma \subset (\mathcal{Q}_\gamma)' \cap (\mathcal{M}_\gamma)' = \mathcal{S}_\gamma$.
It follows that $(\mathcal{Q}_\gamma)' \cap \mathcal{Q}_\gamma = \mathcal{S}_\gamma$ a.e., for as $I \in \mathcal{D}$, both $\mathcal{Q}_\gamma$ and
$(\mathcal{Q}_\gamma)'$ contain $\mathcal{S}_\gamma$, so that $\mathcal{Q}_\gamma$ is a factor a.e.

7. <u>Decomposition</u> <u>of</u> <u>a</u> <u>group</u> <u>representation</u> <u>into</u> <u>irreducible</u>
<u>representations</u>. We show next that every measurable unitary representation
of a separable locally compact group is a kind of direct integral of irreducible continuous unitary representations. This generalizes well-known
results of Stone and Ambrose concerning locally compact abelian groups (but
its application to the special case yields a result which is considerably

less sharp than either that of Stone or that of Ambrose), and similarly generalizes a well-known analogous theorem for compact groups. In view of the known correspondence between positive definite functions on groups and continuous unitary representations of groups [4], our result generalizes the representation theorem for positive definite functions on locally compact abelian groups by showing that on a separable locally compact group, every measurable positive definite function can be represented as an integral of "elementary" positive definite function, where an "elementary" function is defined as one which is not a nontrivial convex linear combination of two other such functions (or alternatively, as one for which the associated group representation is irreducible). A result closely resembling that presented in this section has been announced by F. Mautner [5] and is proved by him apparently with the use of his result resembling our theorem on maximal decompositions (see Section 5), which we use in the following.

$\quad$ **Definition 7.1.** Let U be a unitary representation of the topological group G on a Hilbert space $\mathcal{H}$. We say that U is <u>decomposed into irreducible representations</u> by the (strong or weak) decomposition $\mathcal{H} = \int \mathcal{H}_p \, dr(p)$ if for every $a \in G$, $U(a)$ is decomposable, and if for nearly all $p \in R$, there is an irreducible unitary representation U_p of G such that $U(a)$ is the decomposition of $U(a)$. We then say that U is the (strong or weak) direct integral of the U_p, or symbolically, $U = \int U_p \, dr(p)$. If G is locally compact, U is called <u>measurable</u> if $(U(a)x,\, y)$ is measurable on G relative to Haar measure for all x and y in $\mathcal{H}$ (actually, if G is separable such a representation is necessarily strongly continuous; cf. [12]).

$\quad$ The regularity conditions which the method of proof of the following theorem could be used to establish are significantly stronger than those implied by the theorem. In particular it is possible to define in a natural fashion, in case the representation has a cyclic vector, for all p in the perfect measure space M, a continuous unitary representation U_p, such that $(U_p(a)x(p), y(p))$ is jointly continuous in p and a for x and y ranging over a certain dense subset of $\mathcal{H}$, as well as with U_p irreducible a.e. and $U = \int U_p \, dr(p)$. The method of proof also yields a decomposition for strongly continuous representations of inseparable groups, in which the constituents are irreducible in a kind of average sense (as in Lemma 4.2, but with continuous functions of γ.

THEOREM 6. <u>Every</u> <u>measurable</u> <u>unitary</u> <u>representation</u> <u>of</u> <u>a</u> <u>separable</u> <u>locally</u> <u>compact</u> <u>group</u> G <u>is</u> <u>a</u> <u>direct</u> <u>integral</u> <u>of</u> <u>strongly</u> <u>continuous</u> <u>irreducible</u> <u>unitary</u> <u>representations</u> <u>of</u> G.

Let U be a given strongly continuous unitary representation of G on the Hilbert space $\mathcal{H}$. We put $\mathcal{Q}_o$ for the collection (actually, as is readily shown, a SA algebra; cf. [9]) of all operators on $\mathcal{H}$ of the form $\int U(a)f(a)da$ with $f \in L_1(G)$, where as in [9], $\int U(a)f(a)da$ designates the operator which takes an arbitrary element $x \in \mathcal{H}$ into the strong integral $\int U(a)xf(a)da$. (For a proof of the existence of this integral and for other facts concerning the operator thereby defined, cf. [9], and [8], esp. p. 83, and 84.) Let $\mathcal{Q}$ be the uniform closure of $\mathcal{Q}_o$, so $\mathcal{Q}$ is a C*-algebra. Now the mapping $f \longrightarrow \int U(a)f(a)da$ is continuous on $L_1(G)$ to $\mathcal{Q}_o$, and $L_1(G)$ is separable, for the topological separability of G implies the separability of G as a measure space (relative to a regular measure) which in turn implies the separability of $L_1(G)$. It results that $\mathcal{Q}_o$ is separable, and hence $\mathcal{Q}$ is separable.

If z_1 is an arbitrary nonzero element of $\mathcal{H}$, the closure of $\mathcal{Q}z_1$ is a closed linear manifold $\mathcal{H}^{(1)}$ which is invariant under the $U(a)$ (recalling that $\mathcal{Q}$ is invariant under multiplication by $U(a)$) for $a \in G$. If z_2 is an arbitrary nonzero element in the orthogonal complement $\mathcal{H}^{(1)}$

of $\mathcal{H}^{(1)}$ in $\mathcal{H}$, then the closure of Qz_2 is a closed linear manifold $\mathcal{H}^{(2)}$ in $\mathcal{H}$ which is invariant under the $U(a)$ and orthogonal to $\mathcal{H}^{(1)}$. It follows readily by transfinite induction that there exists a collection $\mathcal{H}(\xi)$ $(\xi \in \Xi)$ of closed linear subspaces of $\mathcal{H}$, mutually orthogonal, with direct sum equal to $\mathcal{H}$, and each invariant under the $U(a)$ and containing an element z_ξ such that Qz_ξ is dense in $\mathcal{H}^{(\xi)}$. This shows that it is sufficient to consider the case in which Q is cyclic on $\mathcal{H}$. For suppose the result has been established in this case. Then if $U^{(\xi)}$ is the contraction of U to $H^{(\xi)}$, for each ξ there is a measure space Γ_ξ and decompositions $\mathcal{H}^{(\xi)} = \int \mathcal{H}_\gamma^{(\xi)} \, d\mu_\xi(\gamma)$ and $U^{(\xi)} = \int U_\gamma^{(\xi)} \, d\mu_\xi(\gamma)$. Let Γ be the measure space whose set of points is $\bigcup_{\xi \in \Xi} \Gamma_\xi$ (we can and shall require that the Γ_ξ are mutually disjoint), in which a σ-finite measurable set is one which meets at most countably many Γ_ξ, and meets each Γ_ξ in a measurable set, and in which the measure μ of such a measurable set is the sum of the μ_ξ-measures of its intersections with the Γ_ξ. It is not difficult to verify that $\mathcal{H}$ is the direct integral of the $\mathcal{H}_\gamma^{(\xi)}$, over (Γ, μ), the only condition which is not trivially verifiable being 2a) (note that as Q is separable, so is Qz for any z, so that the $\mathcal{H}^{(\xi)}$ are separable, and we can take the direct integrals of the $\mathcal{H}_\gamma^{(\xi)}$ to be strong). This follows from the fact that if z satisfies the condition in 2a), then $(z(p), z(p)) = 0$, except on a σ-finite set of p's, say for $p \in \bigcup_{i=1}^{\infty} \Gamma_{\xi_i}$, and we can set $z' = \sum_i z_i'$, where z_i' is such that $z_i'(p) = z(p)$ a.e. for $p \in \Gamma_{\xi_i}$, and $z_i'(p) = 0$ for other values of p, the sum which defines z' being convergent because $(z_i', z_j') = \int_\Gamma (z_i'(p), z_j'(p)) d\mu(p) = 0$ when $i \neq j$, and $\sum_i \| z_i' \|^2 = \sum_i \int_\Gamma \| z_i'(p) \|^2 d\mu_{\xi_i}(p) = \int_\Gamma \| z(p) \|^2 \, d\mu(p)$. It is clear that nearly all the $U_\gamma^{(\xi)}$ are irreducible and that $U = \int_\Gamma U_\gamma^{(\xi)} \, d\mu(p)$.

Suppose now that $\mathcal{A}$ has the normalized cyclic element z in $\mathcal{H}$, and let $\mathcal{C}$ be a W*-algebra which is maximal abelian and self-adjoint in $\mathcal{A}'$, $\mathcal{C}$ exists by Zorn's principle. We can now apply Theorems 1, 2, 3, and 4. Utilizing the notations of these theorems, $\varphi_\gamma(\mathcal{A})$ is a.e. irreducible. Now every (uniformly) continuous self-adjoint representation φ of $\mathcal{A}$ induces a unique continuous unitary representation V of G such that $\varphi\left(\int U(a)f(a)da\right) = \int V(a)f(a)da$ for $f \in L_1(G)$ and with the property that φ is irreducible if and only if V is (see [8] and [9]). If we put U_γ for the representation of G induced by φ_γ , it follows that U_γ is irreducible a.e. and that $U = \int U_\gamma d\mu(\gamma)$.

8. __Decomposition of an invariant measure into ergodic parts.__
We show in this section that a regular measure on a compact metric space which is invariant under a group of homeomorphisms can be represented as a kind of direct integral of ergodic measures on the space. We recall that an ergodic measure is one relative to which every invariant measurable set is either of measure zero or has complement of measure zero.

__Definition 8.1.__ A finite measure m on a σ-ring $\mathcal{F}$ is said to be a direct integral of measures m_p, where p ranges over the set R of a measure space $M = (R, \mathcal{R}, r)$, if for each $p \in R$ m_p is a finite measure on $\mathcal{F}$, and if also for each $E \in \mathcal{F}$, $m_p(E)$ is integrable on M and $\int m_p(E)dr(p) = m(E)$.

The proof of the following theorem yields a kind of maximal decomposition of invariant measures into invariant submeasures in the inseparable (compact) as well as separable (compact metric) case, but we are unable at present to establish ergodicity of the submeasures except in the separable case. A number of similar decompositions have been obtained by quite different methods, for the cases of one-parameter and infinite cyclic groups, the first such result being due to von Neumann, and the most general one being that in [2a] which applies to a class of separable measure spaces including the one considered here.

THEOREM 7. **A regular measure on a compact metric space** M **which is invariant under a group** G **of homeomorphisms of** M **is a direct integral of** G-**ergodic regular measures on** M.

There is clearly no loss of generality in assuming that $m(M) = 1$, where m is the measure in question. We call a bounded measurable function f on M _invariant_ if $f(a(x)) = f(x)$ a.e. on M for all $a \in G$. Let $\mathcal{H}$ be the Hilbert space of all complex-valued functions square-integrable relative to m, the inner product of two elements f and g of $\mathcal{H}$ being defined as $\int_M f(x)\overline{g}(x)dm(x)$. Let Q be the algebra of all operators Q_k on $\mathcal{H}$ of the form $f(x) \longrightarrow k(x)f(x)$, $f \in L_2(M, m)$, where k is a continuous complex-valued function on M, and let C be the algebra of all Q_k with k complex-valued, bounded, measurable, and invariant. We show next that Q is separable in the uniform topology and that C is a W*-algebra.

Let $\{N_i; i = 1, 2, \ldots\}$ be a basis for the open sets in M, and let $\{f_{in}; n = 1, 2, \ldots\}$ be for each i a sequence of continuous functions on M which are uniformly bounded and converge (pointwise) to the characteristic function of N_i. (E.g., if $\{C_{in}\}$ is a monotone increasing sequence of closed subsets of N_i such that $N_i = \bigcup_n C_{in}$, then f_{in} can be taken to be a continuous function with values in $[0, 1]$ which is 1 on C_{in} and 0 outside of N_i, such a function existing by Urysohn's lemma and the normality of a compact Hausdorff space). Then the rational linear combinations of the f_{in} are dense in $C(M)$. For otherwise, by the Hahn-Banach theorem there would exist a nonzero continuous linear functional Φ on $C(M)$ which vanishes on the f_{in}. Now it is known that every such functional has the form $\Phi(f) = \int_M f(x)dn(x)$, for some regular countably-additive set function n on M. It follows easily that $\lim_n \Phi(f_{in}) =$

$\int_{N_i} dn(x) = n(N_i)$, so that n vanishes on all the N_i. It is not difficult to show that any finite union of the N_i differs by a set on which Var n is arbitrarily small from a finite disjoint union of N_i's, which implies that n vanishes on all finite unions of the N_i, and hence on all open sets, and so by regularity vanishes identically. Thus the f_{in} are fundamental in $C(M)$. It follows that $C(M)$ is separable, and as the map $k \longrightarrow Q_k$ is continuous on $C(M)$ to the operators on $\mathcal{H}$ in the uniform topology (in fact $\|k\| \geq \|Q_k\|$), the image $\mathcal{Q}$ must be separable.

For $a \in G$, let U_a be the operator on $\mathcal{H}$ defined by the equation $(U_a f)(x) = f(a(x))$, $f \in \mathcal{H}$. Then it is easily seen that a bounded measurable complex-valued function k on M is invariant if and only if $U_a Q_k = Q_k U_a$ for all $a \in G$. It follows that if $\mathcal{M}$ is the algebra of all Q_k with bounded measurable k, then $C = \mathcal{M} \cap [U_a | a \in G]'$. Now it is known [15] that $\mathcal{M} = \mathcal{M}'$, so that in particular $\mathcal{M}$ is weakly closed, and as it is easily verified that $Q_{\bar{k}} = (Q_k)^*$, $\mathcal{M}$ is SA and so a W*-algebra. Plainly, $[U_a | a \in G]'$ is weakly closed, and it is easily seen that U_a is unitary, so that $(U_a)^* = U_{a^{-1}}$ showing that $[U_a | a \in G]$ is SA. Hence $[U_a | a \in G]'$ is a W*-algebra. Thus C is a W*-algebra containing the identity.

Now let z be the function which is identically unity on M. Then $\mathcal{Q}z$ consists of all continuous functions on M, and so, by virtue of the regularity of m, $\mathcal{Q}z$ is dense in $\mathcal{H}$. It follows that the conditions of Theorem 1 are satisfied, and hence for any $T \in \mathcal{Q}$ and $S \in C$,

$$(TSz, z) = \int_\Gamma S(\gamma)\, \omega_\gamma(T)\, d\mu(\gamma),$$

with Γ, ω_γ, and μ as in Theorem 1. Now the states of $\mathcal{Q}$ are well known; for each ω_γ there is a regular measure m_γ on M such that $\omega_\gamma(Q_k) = \int k(x) dm_\gamma(x)$ for all $k \in C(M)$. We show next that for almost all γ, m_γ is an invariant G-ergodic measure.

It is easily seen that $U_a Q_k U_{a-1} = Q_{U_{ak}}$, so that $U_a T U_{a-1} \in \mathcal{A}$ if $T \in \mathcal{A}$, and $(U_a T U_{a-1} z, z) = \int S(\gamma) \, \omega_\gamma (U_a T U_{a-1}) d\mu(\gamma)$. On the other hand, if $T = Q_k$ and $S = Q_p$ with $T \in \mathcal{A}$ and $S \in \mathcal{C}$, then $(TSz, z) = \int_M k(x)p(x)dm(x)$ and $(U_a T U_{a-1} Sz, z) = \int k(a(x))p(x) \, dm(x) = \int k(x)p(x)dm(x)$ (for m and p are invariant) $= (TSz, z)$. It results that $\int S(\gamma) \, \omega_\gamma(U_a T U_{a-1})d\mu(\gamma) = \int S(\gamma) \, \omega_\gamma(T) \, d\mu(\gamma)$. It follows from the arbitrary character of S (every bounded measurable function on Γ being an $S(.)$) that $\omega_\gamma(U_a T U_{a-1}) = \omega_\gamma(T)$ for almost all γ, and since both sides represent continuous functions, the equality for all γ follows. But if $T = Q_k$, $\omega_\gamma(T) = \int k(x)dm_\gamma(x)$ and $\omega_\gamma(U_a T U_{a-1}) = \int k(a(x))dm_\gamma(x)$, so for all continuous functions k on M, $\int k(x)dm_\gamma(x) = \int k(a(x))dm_\gamma(x)$. It follows that m_γ is invariant for all γ.

We have for any $k \in \mathcal{C}(M)$, putting $T = Q_k$ and $S = I$ in the above formula, that $\int k(x)dm(x) = \int_\Gamma \left[\int_M k(x)dm_\gamma(x) \right] d\mu(\gamma)$. Now if $\mathcal{K}$ is the set of all bounded Baire functions k on M for which this equation holds, it is easily seen that $\mathcal{K}$ is closed under bounded point-wise convergence, and as $\mathcal{K}$ contains all continuous functions, it consists of all bounded Baire functions. Now if E is any Borel measurable set, its characteristic function is Baire and so $m(E) = \int_\Gamma m_\gamma(E) \, d\mu(\gamma)$. Thus m is the direct integral of the m_γ over (Γ, μ).

It remains only to show that m_γ is a.e. ergodic (in fact the preceding decomposition of m into invariant sub-measures is valid without the separability assumption on M). Now the ergodic invariant regular probability measures on a compact space are precisely the extreme points of the set of all invariant regular probability measures on the space (the proof of this in [9] is for the group of reals under addition, but applies to an arbitrary group with trivial modifications). The set of invariant regular probability measures n on M is also known to be in one-to-one convex linear correspondence with the set $\sum$ of all invariant states ν on $\mathcal{A}$

44   I. E. Segal

(ν being invariant if $\nu(U_a T U_{a^{-1}}) = \nu(T)$ for $T \in A$ and $a \in G$), where
n and ν correspond if $\nu(Q_k) = \int k(x) dn(x)$ for all $k \in C(M)$. Now
$\sum$ is a convex set which is compact in the weak topology (recalling that
the state space of a C$*$-algebra with an identity is compact). Moreover,
$\sum$ is metrizable, for if $\left\{ T_i \ (i = 1, 2, \ldots) \right\}$ is a countable dense sub-
set of Q, with no $T_i = 0$, the metric $d(n, p) = \sum_i 2^{-i} \| T_i \|^{-1} |n(T_i) -$
$p(T_i)|$ is easily seen to induce a topology on $\sum$ identical with the weak
topology.

It follows, by an argument used in the proof of Theorem 4, that
if m_γ is not ergodic a.e., then there exist for each γ invariant states
ρ_γ and σ_γ such that 1) $\omega_\gamma = (1/2)(\rho_\gamma + \sigma_\gamma)$ for all γ; 2) if
$T \in Q$, $\rho_\gamma(T)$ and $\sigma_\gamma(T)$ are Borel functions on Γ; 3) $\rho_\gamma \neq \sigma_\gamma$ for
a measurable set of γ's of positive measure. As before, there exists for
each γ an operator S_γ in $(\varphi_\gamma(A))'$ such that $\rho_\gamma(T) =$
$(S_\gamma \varphi_\gamma(T) z(\gamma), z(\gamma))$ and $\| S_\gamma \| \leq 2$. Now $(S_\gamma \eta_\gamma(X), \eta_\gamma(Y)) =$
$(S_\gamma \varphi_\gamma(Y*X) z(\gamma), z(\gamma)) = \rho_\gamma(Y*X)$, and is a measurable function of γ.
It follows that $(S_\gamma x(\gamma), y(\gamma))$ is a measurable function of γ for x
and y in H, and this function is integrable for $|(S_\gamma x(\gamma), y(\gamma))| \leq$
$2 \| x(\gamma) \| \ \| y(\gamma) \|$, which bound is integrable by Schwarz' inequality.
Hence there is a decomposable operator S on H for which $\int S_\gamma d\mu(\gamma)$
is a decomposition. By Theorem 2, $S \in Q'$. We show next that $Q' = M$,
so that S is a multiplication by a bounded measurable function on M.
Now if $\left\{ f_n \right\}$ is a sequence of bounded measurable functions on M which are
uniformly bounded and which converge a.e. to a function f, then Q_{f_n} converges weakly to Q_f, by a simple computation. On any finite regular
measure space, every bounded measurable function is a limit a.e. of a
bounded sequence of continuous functions. It follows that the weak closure
Q_w of Q contains M. Hence $Q_w' \subset M'$, but $Q_w = Q''$, so
$Q_w' = Q'$, and $Q' \subset M' = M$.

Thus $S \in \mathcal{M}$ and so $S = Q_k$. Moreover, $S \in \mathcal{C}$, for if a is arbitrary in G and T arbitrary in Q, then by the invariance of ρ_γ,

$$(S_\gamma \, \varphi_\gamma (U_a TU_{a^{-1}}) z(\gamma), \, z(\gamma)) = (S_\gamma \, \varphi_\gamma (T) z(\gamma), \, z(\gamma)).$$

Integration over Γ of this equation shows that $(SU_a TU_{a^{-1}} z, \, z) = (STz, \, z)$ (noting that $(U_a TU_{a^{-1}} z)(\gamma) = \varphi_\gamma (U_a TU_{a^{-1}}) z(\gamma)$, by Corollary 2.1). If $S = Q_k$ and $T = Q_p$, this means that $\int k(x) p(a(x)) dm(x) = \int k(x) p(x) dm(x)$, which implies that $\int k(a^{-1}(x)) p(x) dm(x) = \int k(x) p(x) dm(x)$, from which it follows readily that $k(a^{-1}(x)) = k(x)$ a.e. for each $a \in G$. That is, $S \in \mathcal{C}$, so S_γ is a.e. a scalar multiple of the identity, and $\rho_\gamma = \sigma_\gamma = \omega_\gamma$ a.e., a contradiction. Hence m_γ is a.e. ergodic.

9. <u>The Fourier transform for separable unimodular groups</u>. We show in the present section how the Fourier transform as defined in [11] can be correlated with the Fourier transform as an integral whose kernel is an irreducible group representation. If f is an integrable function on the locally compact abelian group G, its Fourier transform is usually defined as the function F on the character group $G*$ of G, defined by the equation $F(x*) = \int_G x*(x) f(x) dx$. The generalized (Weil-Krein) Plancherel theorem then asserts that $\int_{G*} |F(x*)|^2 dx* = \int_G |f(x)|^2 \, dx$, for $f \in L_2(G)$. The Fourier transform can be extended to compact (not necessarily abelian) groups by replacing $G*$ by the collection of continuous irreducible unitary representations of G (which is simply the character group when G is abelian); one has then $F(\rho) = \int_G \rho(x) f(x) dx$ and the generalized Plancherel theorem (usually called the Peter-Weyl theorem in this context) asserts that $\int_G |f(x)|^2 \, dx = \sum_\rho \mathrm{tr}((F(\rho))*F(\rho)) d(\rho)$, where $d(\rho)$ is the degree of ρ, tr denotes the usual trace, and the sum is over any collection of representatives of equivalence classes of irreducible representations of G.

In the case of an arbitrary separable unimodular group, it turns out that the same formal relations are valid, provided "irreducible unitary representation" is replaced by "two-sided irreducible unitary representation". As indicated in [10], this does not materially affect the situation in groups which are either compact or abelian. More specifically, in [11] it is shown that if the Fourier transform is defined through the use of the von Neumann reduction theory, then the Plancherel formula for a separable unimodular group holds, the trace now being that defined by Murray and von Neumann for factors, and the integration being over a measure-theoretic analog of $G*$. As it can be verified that the reduction obtained in Theorem 2 satisfies von Neumann's conditions (cf. the last theorem in this paper), the Plancherel transform $F(\gamma)$ of a function $f \in L_1(G) \cap L_2(G)$ can also be defined through the use of the present decomposition theory. We shall show in this section that the Plancherel transform of f can also be obtained as follows: for each $\gamma \in \Gamma$, where (Γ, μ) is the perfect measure space on which the decomposition is built, there is a two-sided continuous unitary representation $\{L_\gamma, R_\gamma\}$, where L_γ and R_γ are respectively the left and right ordinary representations of which the two-sided representation is composed, which is a.e. irreducible, and such that $F(\gamma) = \int_G L_\gamma(a)f(a)da$.

We begin by considering the decomposition of conjugations in suitable situations. We recall that a function J on a Hilbert space $\mathcal{H}$ to itself is called a conjugation if it satisfies the conditions: 1) $J^2 = I$, 2) $(Jx, Jy) = (y, x)$ for all x and y in $\mathcal{H}$; and that it has the properties $J(x + y) = Jx + Jy$, and $J(\alpha x) = \bar{\alpha} x$ for all x and y in $\mathcal{H}$ and complex α. It follows that the map $W \longrightarrow JWJ$ is a ring automorphism of the set of all operators on $\mathcal{H}$, and that $(JWJ)* = JW*J$. We denote JWJ by W^J, and designate the automorphism $W \longrightarrow W^J$ by $\tilde{J}$.

THEOREM 8. <u>With the notation of Theorem 1, let J be a conjugation of $\mathcal{H}$ such that $S^J = S*$ for all $S \in C$, and $Jz = z$. Then there exists for each $\gamma \in \Gamma$ a conjugation J_γ on $\mathcal{H}_\gamma$ such that for any</u>

x <u>and</u> y <u>in</u> $\mathcal{H}$, $(Jx, y) = \int_{\Gamma} (J_{\gamma} \, x(\gamma), y(\gamma)) d\mu(\gamma).$

We first define J_{γ} on $\eta_{\gamma}(A)$ as follows: $J_{\gamma} \, \eta_{\gamma}(T) = \eta_{\gamma}(T^{J})$. To see that this definition is single-valued, observe that if $\eta_{\gamma}(T) = \eta_{\gamma}(W)$, then $(\eta_{\gamma}(T) - \eta_{\gamma}(W), \eta_{\gamma}(T) - \eta_{\gamma}(W)) = 0$, so that $\omega((T - W)^{*}(T - W)) = 0$. Now ω is transformed into $\bar{\omega}$ by $(\tilde{J})^{*}$ so that $\omega(J(T - W)^{*}(T - W)J) = 0 = \omega((J(T - W)J)^{*}(J(T - W)J)) = (\eta_{\gamma}(T^{J}) - \eta_{\gamma}(W^{J}), \eta_{\gamma}(T^{J}) - \eta_{\gamma}(W^{J}))$, so that $\eta_{\gamma}(T^{J}) = \eta_{\gamma}(W^{J})$.

We show next that for all γ and for $T \in Q$, $\omega_{\gamma}(T^{J}) = \bar{\omega}_{\gamma}(T)$. Let S be an arbitrary self-adjoint operator in C. Then $\omega(ST^{J}) = \int S(\gamma) \, \omega_{\gamma}(T^{J}) d\mu(\gamma)$. On the other hand, $\omega(ST^{J}) = \omega(S^{J}T^{J})$ (for a SA element of C is invariant under $\tilde{J}$) $= \omega((ST)^{J}) = \bar{\omega}(ST) = \int S(\gamma) \, \omega_{\gamma}(T) d\mu(\gamma)$. As $S = S^{*}$, it results that $\int S(\gamma) \left\{ \omega_{\gamma}(T^{J}) - \bar{\omega}_{\gamma}(T) \right\} d\mu(\gamma) = 0$. As $S(.)$ can then be an arbitrary real-valued bounded measurable function on Γ, it results that $\omega_{\gamma}(T^{J}) - \bar{\omega}_{\gamma}(T) = 0$ a.e., and since the left side is a continuous function on Γ, we have $\omega_{\gamma}(T^{J}) = \bar{\omega}_{\gamma}(T)$.

Now for any T and W in Q we have $(J_{\gamma} \, \eta_{\gamma}(T), J_{\gamma} \, \eta_{\gamma}(W)) = (\eta_{\gamma}(T^{J}), \eta_{\gamma}(W^{J})) = \omega_{\gamma}(W^{J*}T^{J}) = \omega_{\gamma}(W^{*J}T^{J}) = \omega_{\gamma}((W^{*}T)^{J}) = \bar{\omega}_{\gamma}(W^{*}T) = \overline{(\eta_{\gamma}(T), \eta_{\gamma}(W))}$. In particular, $\| J_{\gamma} \, \eta_{\gamma}(T) \| \leq \| \eta_{\gamma}(T) \|$, so that J_{γ} is bounded on $\eta_{\gamma}(Q)$, and therefore has a unique continuous extension to the closure $\mathcal{H}_{\gamma}$ of $\eta_{\gamma}(Q)$; we denote this extension also by J_{γ}. From the equation $(J_{\gamma} \, \eta_{\gamma}(T), J_{\gamma} \, \eta_{\gamma}(W)) = \overline{(\eta_{\gamma}(T), \eta_{\gamma}(W))}$ it follows by continuity that for arbitrary x_{γ} and y_{γ} in $\mathcal{H}_{\gamma}$, $(J_{\gamma} \, x_{\gamma}, J_{\gamma} \, y_{\gamma}) = \overline{(x_{\gamma}, y_{\gamma})}$. Now $J_{\gamma}^{2} \, \eta_{\gamma}(T) = J_{\gamma}(J_{\gamma} \, \eta_{\gamma}(T)) = J_{\gamma} \, \eta_{\gamma}(T^{J}) = \eta_{\gamma}(T)$, so that J_{γ}^{2} is the identity on $\eta_{\gamma}(Q)$, and hence also, by continuity, on $\mathcal{H}_{\gamma}$. Thus J_{γ} is a conjugation.

It remains to show that for arbitrary x and y in $\mathcal{H}$, $(Jx, y) = \int_{\Gamma} (J_{\gamma} \, x(\gamma), y(\gamma)) d\mu(\gamma)$. Now if $x = Tz$ and $y = Wz$ with

T and W in $\mathcal{Q}$, $(Jx, y) = (JTz, Wz) = (W*JTz, z) = (W*T^J z, z)$ (using the fact that $Jz = z$) $= \int \omega_\gamma (W*T^J) d\mu(\gamma) = \int (\eta_\gamma(T^J),\ \eta_\gamma(W)) d\mu(\gamma) = \int (J_\gamma \eta_\gamma(T),\ \eta_\gamma(W)) d\mu(\gamma)$. Thus the equation is valid for a dense set of x and y's, and it follows as in the first part of the paper that it is valid for all x and y in $\mathcal{H}$. When ω_γ is not a state, J_γ can of course be defined arbitrarily.

The next theorem asserts that the conditions of the preceding theorem are satisfied (with a suitable choice for z) in the case of a certain conjugation on $L_2(G)$ for a unimodular group G.

THEOREM 9. <u>Let</u> G <u>be a separable unimodular locally compact group, and let</u> $\mathcal{Q}$ <u>be the C*-algebra generated by all operators on</u> $\mathcal{H} = L_2(G)$ <u>of the form</u> $L_f R_g$, <u>with</u> f <u>and</u> g <u>in</u> $L_1(G)$, <u>where</u> L_f <u>and</u> R_g <u>are respectively left convolution by</u> f <u>and right convolution by</u> g. <u>Let</u> C <u>be the center of the weak closure of</u> $\mathcal{Q}$. <u>Then if</u> J <u>is the conjugation on</u> $\mathcal{H}$ <u>defined by the equation</u> $Jf = f*$ <u>for</u> $f \in \mathcal{H}$, <u>where</u> $f*(x) = \overline{f}(x^{-1})$, <u>every self-adjoint element of</u> C <u>is invariant under the automorphism induced by</u> J (<u>i.e.</u> $JSJ = S^*$ <u>if</u> $S \in C$); <u>there exists an element</u> z <u>in</u> $\mathcal{H}$ <u>such that</u> $\mathcal{Q}z$ <u>is dense in</u> $\mathcal{H}$ <u>and</u> $Jz = z$; <u>and</u> $\mathcal{Q}' = C$.

We show to begin with that $C = \mathcal{Q}'$ and that the weak closure of $\mathcal{Q}$ is the W*-algebra generated by L and R, where L and R are respectively the W*-algebras generated by the L_a and R_a, these operators being defined by the equations $(L_a f)(x) = f(a^{-1}x)$ and $(R_a f)(x) = f(xa)$, $f \in \mathcal{H}$ and $a \in G$. Clearly $T \in \mathcal{Q}'$ if and only if $TL_f R_g = L_f R_g T$ for all f and g in $L_1(G)$, i.e., if $TL_f R_g h = L_f R_g Th$ for such f and g and all $h \in \mathcal{H}$. Now if $\{g_n\}$ is a sequence in $L_1(G)$ such that $h * g_n \longrightarrow h$ and $(Th) * g_n \longrightarrow Th$, it results from the equation $TL_f R_{g_n} h = L_f R_{g_n} Th$ that $TL_f h = L_f Th$. Hence $TL_f = L_f T$, and as $\mathcal{L}$ is generated by the L_f (cf. [10]), this shows that $T \in \mathcal{L}'$. Similarly $T \in \mathcal{R}'$, and so we have $\mathcal{Q}' \subset \mathcal{L}' \cap \mathcal{R}'$. It is shown in [10] that $\mathcal{L}' = \mathcal{R}$, so $\mathcal{Q}' \subset \mathcal{R} \cap \mathcal{R}'$, which shows that $\mathcal{Q}'$ is abelian. It follows that the center of $\mathcal{Q}^*$ is $\mathcal{Q}'$, and as $\mathcal{Q}$ is SA, its weak closure is $\mathcal{Q}''$, so that $C = \mathcal{Q}'$. On the other hand, $L_f \in \mathcal{L}$ and $R_f \in \mathcal{R}$ for all $f \in L_1(G)$ (loc. cit.), which implies that $\mathcal{Q} \subset \mathcal{L} \cap \mathcal{R}$. Hence $\mathcal{Q}' \supset \mathcal{L}' \cup \mathcal{R}'$ and it follows that $\mathcal{Q}' = \mathcal{L}' \cap \mathcal{R}'$ or $\mathcal{Q}'' = \mathcal{L} \cup \mathcal{R}$.

Next we show that for an arbitrary element S of C, $S^J = S^*$. The mapping $T \longrightarrow T^J$ is easily seen to be continuous in the strong operator topology. As the finite linear combinations of projections in C are strongly dense in C, it therefore suffices to prove $S^J = S^*$ for the case when S is such a linear combination. As $\tilde{J}$ is conjugate linear, it is enough to show that $P^J = P$ for every projection P in C. Now let $\mathcal{M}$ be the range of such a projection P. It is shown in [11] that $\mathcal{M}$ is then a two-sided ideal in the L_2-system of G in the sense of Ambrose [2]. According to a theorem of Ambrose (loc. cit. Th. 7), every such ideal is invariant under J. Hence for $x \in \mathcal{H}$, $JPx \in \mathcal{M}$, i.e., $P(JPx) = JPx$, or $PJP = JP$. Multiplying the last equation on the left by J shows that $P^J P = P$. Now P is SA, so $(P^J P)^* = P$ and $PP^J = P$. Applying $\tilde{J}$ to both sides of the last equation shows that $P^J P = P^J$, so $P = P^J$.

It remains to show that there exists an element z of H such that $\mathcal{Q}z$ is dense in $\mathcal{H}$ and $Jz = z$. Let $\{z_i\}$ be a family of elements of $\mathcal{H}$ which is maximal with respect to the properties 1) $Jz_i = z_i$ and $z_i \neq 0$, 2) $\mathcal{Q}z_i$ is orthogonal to $\mathcal{Q}z_j$ if $i \neq j$. Then the index set over which i ranges is at most countable, for the closures of the $\mathcal{Q}z_i$ constitute a family of mutually orthogonal closed linear subspaces of $\mathcal{H}$, which by the separability of $\mathcal{H}$ must be at most countable. We assume that $i = 1, 2, \ldots$ and put $z = \sum_n n^{-2} \| z_n \|^{-1} z_n$. Plainly $Jz = z$, and we show finally that $\mathcal{Q}z$ is dense in $\mathcal{H}$.

Assume on the contrary that $\mathcal{Q}z$ is not dense in $\mathcal{H}$. Then there exists a nonzero element x in $\mathcal{H}$ which is orthogonal to $\mathcal{Q}z$. Let $\mathcal{M}_1$ be the closure of $\mathcal{Q}z_1$ and P_1 the projection operator on $\mathcal{H}$ with range $\mathcal{M}_1$. We have $(Tz, x) = 0$ for $T \in \mathcal{Q}$, so $(S*Tz, x) = 0$ for S and T in $\mathcal{Q}$, or $(Tz, Sx) = 0$ for such S and T. It is easy to deduce that the last equation is valid for all S and T in the weak closure of $\mathcal{Q}$. Now it is easily verified that $\mathcal{M}_1$ is invariant under $\mathcal{Q}$, so that $P_1 \in \mathcal{Q}' = \mathcal{C}$, and hence $P_1 \in \mathcal{Q}''$. Hence we have in particular, for $T \in \mathcal{Q}$, $(TP_1z, P_1x) = 0$ or $(Tz_1, P_1x) = 0$. Now $P_1x \in \mathcal{M}_1$ but the Tz_1 span $\mathcal{M}_1$, so $P_1x = 0$. As $x \neq 0$, $I - \sum_1 P_1 = Q$ is a nonzero projection in $\mathcal{C}$. Putting w for any nonzero element of $Q\mathcal{H}$ such that $Jw \neq -w$ (obviously such a vector exists) and $z' = w + Jw$, clearly $Jz' = z'$ and $\mathcal{Q}z' = \mathcal{Q}Qz' = Q\mathcal{Q}z' \subset Q\mathcal{H}$, so that $\mathcal{Q}z'$ is orthogonal to all the $\mathcal{Q}z_1$, contradicting the maximality of $\{z_1\}$.

Before proving the result mentioned in the beginning of this section we make appropriate definitions.

<u>Definition 9.1</u>. A <u>two-sided</u> <u>representation</u> <u>of</u> <u>a</u> <u>group</u> G on a Hilbert space $\mathcal{H}$ is a pair (L, R) of one-sided representations of G on $\mathcal{H}$ such that $L(a)R(b) = R(b)L(a)$ for all a and b in G. If G is topological, such a representation is called strongly or weakly continuous if both L and R are (respectively) strongly or weakly continuous. If (L, R) is a two-sided representation of G on $\mathcal{H}$, if each of L and R is unitary, and if J is a conjugation on $\mathcal{H}$ such that $JL(a)J = R(a)$ for all $a \in G$, then the system (L, R, J) is called a <u>two-sided</u> <u>unitary</u> <u>representation</u> of G. A two-sided representation (L, R) is called <u>irre</u>-<u>ducible</u> if the $L(a)$ and $R(b)$ $(a, b \in G)$ leave no closed linear subspace of $\mathcal{H}$ (jointly) invariant other than 0 and $\mathcal{H}$.

The following theorem shows the connection between the Fourier transform as defined directly thru reduction theory and as defined thru the use of an integral whose kernel is a representation.

THEOREM 10. _Let_ G, $\mathcal{H}$, $\mathcal{Q}$, $\mathcal{C}$, J, _and_ z _be as in the preceding theorem, and let_ Γ, μ, _and_ ω_γ _be as in Theorem 1. For every_ f $\in$ $L_1(G)$, _the left and right convolution operators_ L_f _and_ R_f _are decomposable with respect to the reduction of_ $\mathcal{H}$ _described in Theorem 2, with_ M $= (\Gamma, \mu)$. _For almost all_ $\gamma \in \Gamma$ _there is a two-sided strongly continuous unitary irreducible representation_ $\{L_\gamma, R_\gamma, J_\gamma\}$ _of_ G _on_ $\mathcal{H}_\gamma$ _which is almost everywhere on_ (Γ, μ) _irreducible, and such that the decompositions of_ L_f _and_ R_f _are_ $\int_G L_\gamma(a)f(a)da$ _and_ $\int_G R_\gamma(a)f(a)da$ _respectively._

We observe to begin with that for any a $\in$ G and X $\in \mathcal{Q}$, $L_a X$ and $R_a X$ are in $\mathcal{Q}$. For let $\mathcal{Q}_o$ be the algebra generated by the $L_f R_g$ with f and g in $L_1(G)$; as every L_f commutes with every R_g this algebra consists simply of all finite sums of such operators. Now it is easily verified by direct computation that $L_a L_f = L_{f_a}$ and $R_a R_g = R_{g^a}$, where $f_a(x) = f(a^{-1}x)$ and $g^a(x) = g(xa)$. It follows that $\mathcal{Q}_o$ is invariant under left multiplication by the L_a and the R_a, and it is not difficult to deduce by an approximation argument that so also is $\mathcal{Q}$ invariant (cf. [8], p. 80). A trivial modification of a proof in loc. cit. shows also that $R_a X$ and $L_a X$ are continuous functions on G to $\mathcal{Q}$, in the uniform topology on $\mathcal{Q}$.

The remainder of the procedure for obtaining the L_γ and the R_γ is also similar to that used in loc. cit., and we shall merely outline it. We define $\hat{L}_\gamma(a)$ on $\eta_\gamma(A)$ by the equation $\hat{L}_\gamma(a)\eta_\gamma(T) = \eta_\gamma(L_a T)$. It is easily verified that $\hat{L}_\gamma(a)\eta_\gamma(T)$ is single-valued and that for each a $\in$ G, $\hat{L}_\gamma(a)$ is an isometry on $\eta_\gamma(\mathcal{Q})$. It can therefore be uniquely extended to an isometry, denoted by $L_\gamma(a)$, of $\mathcal{H}_\gamma$ into $\mathcal{H}_\gamma$. The mapping a $\longrightarrow \hat{L}_\gamma(a)$ is a representation, and hence so is the mapping

$a \longrightarrow L_\gamma(a)$. Plainly $L_\gamma(e) = I_\gamma$ (where e is the group identity and I_γ the identity operator on $\mathcal{H}_\gamma$), so $L_\gamma(a)L_\gamma(a^{-1}) = L_\gamma(a^{-1})L_\gamma(a) = I_\gamma$, which shows that $L_\gamma(a)$ is unitary. Now the map $a \longrightarrow L_a X$ is continuous on G to $\mathcal{Q}$, and η_γ is continuous on $\mathcal{Q}$ to $\mathcal{H}_\gamma$, so $L_\gamma(a) \eta_\gamma(X)$ is a continuous function on G to $\mathcal{H}_\gamma$, for any fixed $X \in \mathcal{Q}$. It follows by continuity that $L_\gamma(a)x_\gamma$ is continuous as a function on G to $\mathcal{H}_\gamma$ for each fixed $x_\gamma \in \mathcal{H}_\gamma$. Similarly for the definition and properties of R_γ. (These definitions are for the γ such that ω_γ is a state; for the null set of other γ we take L_γ and R_γ to be the identity representation and J_γ to be an arbitrary conjugation on H_γ.

Now $L_a R_b X = R_b L_a X$ for any $X \in \mathcal{Q}$, which implies that $L_\gamma(a)R_\gamma(b) \eta_\gamma(X) = R_\gamma(b)L_\gamma(a) \eta_\gamma(X)$, and as $L_\gamma(a)$ and $R_\gamma(b)$ are bounded and $\eta_\gamma(\mathcal{Q})$ is dense in $\mathcal{H}_\gamma$, it follows that $L_\gamma(a)R_\gamma(b)x_\gamma = R_\gamma(b)L_\gamma(a)x_\gamma$ for all $x_\gamma \in \mathcal{H}_\gamma$, i.e., $L_\gamma(a)$ and $R_\gamma(b)$ commute for all a and b in G. Next, it is easily verified that $JL_a J = R_a$, and it follows that for $X \in \mathcal{Q}$, $JL_a XJ = R_a JXJ$, or $(L_a X)^J = R_a X^J$. Hence $\eta_\gamma((L_a X)^J) = \eta_\gamma(R_a X^J)$, and by the definition of J_γ in the proof of Theorem 8, $J_\gamma \eta_\gamma(L_a X) = R_\gamma(a) \eta_\gamma(X^J)$, or $J_\gamma L_\gamma(a) \eta_\gamma(X) = R_\gamma(a)J_\gamma \eta_\gamma(X)$. Thus the bounded linear operators $L_\gamma(a)$ and $J_\gamma R_\gamma(a)J_\gamma$ agree on the dense set $\eta_\gamma(\mathcal{Q})$, and therefore coincide.

Now if f and g are arbitrary in $L_1(G)$ and X is arbitrary in $\mathcal{Q}$, we have $\varphi_\gamma(L_f R_g) \eta_\gamma(X) = \eta_\gamma(L_f R_g X)$. We note that $\iint L_a R_b X\, f(a)g(b)da\,db$ exists as a strong vector-valued integral (i.e., relative to the uniform topology on $\mathcal{Q}$), and equals $L_f R_g X$ (cf. loc. cit.). As η_γ is a continuous linear operation, it results that $\eta_\gamma(L_f R_g X) = \iint \eta_\gamma(L_a R_b X)\, f(a)g(b)da\,db$, but $\eta_\gamma(L_a R_b X) = L_\gamma(a)R_\gamma(b) \eta_\gamma(X)$, so we have

$$\varphi_\gamma(L_f R_g)x_\gamma = \iint L_\gamma(a)R_\gamma(b)x_\gamma\, f(a)g(b)da\,db$$

for $x_\gamma = \eta_\gamma(X)$. As $\eta_\gamma(\mathcal{Q})$ is dense in $\mathcal{H}_\gamma$, and as $\varphi_\gamma(L_f R_g)$ and $\iint L_\gamma(a)R_\gamma(b)f(a)g(b)da\,db$ are bounded linear operators, it follows that the preceding equation is valid for all $x_\gamma \in \mathcal{H}_\gamma$. Now if $\{g_n\}$ is a sequence in $L_1(G)$ such that $g_n(a) \geq 0$, $\int g_n(a)da = 1$, and g_n vanishes outside of W_n, where $\bigcap_n W_n = \{e\}$, then $L_f R_{g_n}$ is easily seen to converge strongly to L_f, so that L_f is decomposable, and similarly R_g is decomposable. On the other hand, by the Fubini theorem for vector integration $\iint L_\gamma(a) R_\gamma(b) x_\gamma f(a) g_n(b) da\, db = \int R_\gamma(b) [\int L_\gamma(a) x_\gamma f(a) da] g_n(b) db$, which expression is easily seen, by virtue of the strong continuity of R_γ, to converge strongly as $n \longrightarrow \infty$, to $\int L_\gamma(a) x_\gamma f(a) da$. Thus the decomposition of L_f is as stated, and similarly for that of R_f.

It remains only to show the irreducibility a.e. of $\mathcal{H}_\gamma$ under the combined action of the $L_\gamma(a)$ and the $R_\gamma(b)$, a and b being arbitrary in G. Now if a closed linear manifold in $\mathcal{H}_\gamma$ is invariant under the $L_\gamma(a)$ and the $R_\gamma(b)$ it is also invariant under $\varphi_\gamma(L_f R_g)$ for all f and g in $L_1(G)$ (cf. loc. cit.), and hence is invariant under $\varphi_\gamma(Q)$. Now as shown at the end of the proof of the preceding theorem, $C = (Q_w)'$, where Q_w is the weak closure of Q, and it follows that $C = Q'$. This shows that C is maximal abelian in Q'. The separability of $L_1(G)$ together with the continuity of the maps $f \longrightarrow L_f$ and $f \longrightarrow R_f$ on $L_1(G)$ to Q, implies the separability of Q_0, from which the separability of Q follows. Hence Theorem 4 implies that $\varphi_\gamma(Q)$ is irreducible a.e.

<u>Remark 9.1</u>. In the special case (for semi-simple Lie groups, conjecturally the general case) that $\mathcal{L}$ is a direct integral of factors of type I, the situation can be further reduced, in that the corresponding two-sided irreducible representations of the group G arise in an obvious fashion from one-sided representations. Specifically, for almost all γ, there is a Hilbert space $\mathcal{K}_\gamma$, a strongly continuous irreducible (one-sided) representation U_γ of G on $\mathcal{H}_\gamma$, and a conjugation C_γ of $\mathcal{K}_\gamma$, such that the foregoing two-sided representation $\{L_\gamma, R_\gamma, J_\gamma\}$ is unitarily equivalent to the representation $\{L'_\gamma, R'_\gamma, J'_\gamma\}$ of G on the Kronecker

product $\mathcal{H}'_\gamma = \mathcal{K}_\gamma \# \mathcal{K}_\gamma$, where L'_γ, R'_γ, and J'_γ are determined by the
equations $L'_\gamma(a)(x \# y) = (U_\gamma(a)x) \# y$, $R'_\gamma(a)(x \# y) = x \#(C_\gamma U_\gamma(a)C_\gamma y)$, and
$J'_\gamma(x \# y) = (C_\gamma y \# C_\gamma x)$, for all x and y in $\mathcal{K}_\gamma$ and $a \in G$. If $\mathcal{K}_\gamma$ is
taken as $L_2(M)$ for a measure space $M = (R, \mathcal{R}, r)$, then $\mathcal{H}'_\gamma$ can be
taken as $L_2(M \times M)$ and J'_γ can then be defined by the equation
$(J'_\gamma f)(x, y) = \overline{f(y, x)}$, $f \in \mathcal{H}'_\gamma$.

To see this, let $\mathcal{L}_\gamma$ and $\mathcal{R}_\gamma$ be respectively the W*-algebras
generated by the $L_\gamma(a)$ and the $R_\gamma(a)$, $a \in G$, and observe that $\mathcal{L} = \int \mathcal{L}_\gamma \, d\mu(\gamma)$. For if $S \in \int \mathcal{L}_\gamma \, d\mu(\gamma)$, say $S = \int S_\gamma \, d\mu(\gamma)$, then $S_\gamma \in$
$(\mathcal{R}_\gamma)'$ for all γ. Now if $W = R_f$ with $f \in L_1(G)$, then $W = \int W_\gamma \, d\mu(\gamma)$,
where $W_\gamma = \int R_\gamma(a)f(a)da$, and it can be seen that $W_\gamma \in R_\gamma$ (cf. [10]).
Hence S_γ and W_γ commute, and it follows that S and W commute,
which implies $S \in \{R_f\}'$ or $S \in \mathcal{R}' = \mathcal{L}$. Thus $\mathcal{L} \supset \int \mathcal{L}_\gamma \, d\mu(\gamma)$. On the
other hand, it follows from [10] that every element of $\mathcal{L}$ is a strong
sequential limit of (bounded) operators of the form L_f, with $f \in L_2(G)$.
Every such operator in turn is a weak sequential limit of operators of the
form L_f with $f \in L_1(G)$, for if h and g are arbitrary in $L_2(G)$, the
integral $\int f(y)g(y^{-1}x)dy$ exists and by virtue of the boundedness of L_f,
equals $(L_f g)(x)$ (see [11]), and by Fubini's theorem the integral
$\iint f(y)g(y^{-1}x)\overline{h}(x) \, dxdy$ exists. It follows from the Lebesgue convergence
theorem that if $\{K_n\}$ is a sequence of compact subsets of G such that
$K_{n+1} \supset K_n$ and f vanishes nearly everywhere outside of $\bigcup_n K_n$, and if
f_n is the product of f with the characteristic function of K_n, then
$\{L_{f_n}\}$ converges weakly to L_f. As weak and strong sequential limits of
decomposable operators are likewise decomposable, it follows that every
operator in L is decomposable, i.e., $\mathcal{L} \subset \int \mathcal{L}_\gamma \, d\mu(\gamma)$, and hence $\mathcal{L} = \int \mathcal{L}_\gamma \, d\mu(\gamma)$.

Now by the irreducibility a.e. of $\{L_\gamma, R_\gamma, J_\gamma\}$ we have a.e.
$\mathcal{L}_\gamma \cup \mathcal{R}_\gamma = \mathcal{B}_\gamma$, where $\mathcal{B}_\gamma$ is the algebra of all operators on $\mathcal{H}_\gamma$. Clearly

$\mathcal{L}'_\gamma \supset \mathcal{R}_\gamma$. It follows readily as in the proof of Theorem 5 that $\mathcal{L}_\gamma$ and $\mathcal{R}_\gamma$ are factors. Now assuming that $\mathcal{L}_\gamma$ is of type I, we shall show that $\{L_\gamma, R_\gamma, J_\gamma\}$ has the special form given above. For this it is evidently sufficient to establish the following lemma, which includes a result recently announced by Godement [4a].

LEMMA. Let $\{L, R, J\}$ be a two-sided irreducible strongly continuous unitary representation of a topological group G on a Hilbert space $\mathcal{H}$, and let the W*-algebra $\mathcal{L}$ generated by the $L(a)$, $a \in G$, be of type I. Then there exists a one-sided irreducible strongly continuous representation U of G on a Hilbert space $\mathcal{K}$, and a conjugation C of $\mathcal{K}$, such that $\{L, R, J, \mathcal{H}\}$ is unitarily equivalent to the system $\{L', R', J', \mathcal{H}'\}$ where $\mathcal{H}' = \mathcal{K} \# \mathcal{K}$, J' is the conjugation of $\mathcal{H}'$ defined by the equation $J'(x \# y) = Cy \# Cx$, for all x and y in $\mathcal{K}$, and $\mathcal{L}'$ and $\mathcal{R}'$ are the representations of G defined by the equations $L'(a)(x \# y) = (U(a)x) \# y$ and $R'(a)(x \# y) = (x \# CU(a)Cy)$ for all x and y in $\mathcal{K}$.

By [7, pp. 138-9 and 174], $\mathcal{H}$ is unitarily equivalent to $\mathcal{H}' = \mathcal{K}_1 \# \mathcal{K}_2$ for suitable Hilbert spaces $\mathcal{K}_1$ and $\mathcal{K}_2$ in such a way that $\mathcal{L}$ is mapped into the set $\mathcal{L}_1$ of all operators of the form $S \# I$ with S an operator on $\mathcal{K}_1$, and the W*-algebra $\mathcal{R}$ generated by the $R(a)$ is mapped into the set $\mathcal{R}_1$ of all operators of the form $I \# T$ with T an operator on $\mathcal{K}_2$. Now J maps into a conjugation J' of $\mathcal{H}'$ with the property that $J'\mathcal{L}_1 J' = \mathcal{R}_1$. As the dimension of a Hilbert space is the maximal number of mutually orthogonal minimal projections in the algebra of all operators on the space, and as the mapping $X \longrightarrow J'XJ'$ is a ring isomorphism preserving adjoints, $\mathcal{K}_1$ and $\mathcal{K}_2$ have the same dimension and we can set $\mathcal{K}_1 = \mathcal{K}_2 = \mathcal{K}$. Plainly $L(a)$ is mapped by the foregoing equivalence into a unitary operator $L'(a)$ on $\mathcal{K} \# \mathcal{K}$ of the form

L"(a)#I, where the W*-algebra generated by the L'(a), a ∈ G, is $\mathcal{L}_1$. Now it is easily seen that the map T#I ⟶ T from $\mathcal{L}_1$ to the operators on $\mathcal{K}$ is strongly continuous. It follows readily that the map a ⟶ L"(a) is a strongly continuous unitary representation of G on $\mathcal{K}$, and that the strong closure of the algebra generated by the L"(a) is the algebra $\mathcal{B}$ of all operators on $\mathcal{K}$. The latter feature implies that L" is an irreducible representation. Similarly R(a) is mapped by the foregoing equivalence into I#R"(a), where R" is an irreducible strongly continuous irreducible unitary representation of G on $\mathcal{K}$.

For any T ∈ $\mathcal{B}$ we have clearly J'(T#I)J' = I# φ(T), for some function φ on $\mathcal{B}$. It is readily verified that φ is an (adjoint-preserving) ring automorphism of $\mathcal{B}$ of period 2, and with the property that $\varphi(\alpha T)$ = $\bar{\alpha} \varphi(T)$ for complex α and T ∈ $\mathcal{B}$. It is not difficult to deduce that there exists a conjugation J" of $\mathcal{K}$ such that $\varphi(T)$ = J"TJ" for T ∈ $\mathcal{B}$. Now let C' be the conjugation of $\mathcal{H}'$ determined by the equation C'(x#y) = J"y#J"x, for x and y in $\mathcal{K}$. It is easily seen that J'C' is a unitary operator U' on H' with the property that U'*$\mathcal{L}_1$U' = $\mathcal{L}_1$. As $\mathcal{L}_1$ is algebraically isomorphic to $\mathcal{B}$, every automorphism is inner, and so there exists a unitary operator V' in $\mathcal{L}_1$ such that U'*T'U' = V'*T'V' for all T ∈ $\mathcal{L}_1$. It follows from the last equation that U'V'$^{-1}$ ∈ $\mathcal{L}_1'$, so that U'=V'W' with W' a unitary operator in $\mathcal{R}_1$. Evidently V' = V#I and W' = I#W, where V and W are unitary operators on $\mathcal{K}$, and it results that J' = (V#W)C'.

Now J'(T#I)(x#y) = (I# φ(T))J'(x#y) for all x and y in $\mathcal{K}$, and substituting the above expressions for J' and for φ, it is found that (VJ"y)#(WJ"Tx) = (VJ"y)#(J"TJ"WJ"x). It results that WJ"T = J"TJ"WJ", and multiplying on the left by J", it follows that J"WJ" commutes with T. As T is arbitrary in $\mathcal{B}$, this implies that J"WJ" = I and hence W = I. The equation J'^{2} = I implies that J'^{2}(x#y) = x#y for all x and y in $\mathcal{K}$, and

substituting J' = (V#I)C' there results the equation (Vx)#J"VJ"y) = x#y.
Hence V = I and J' = C'. The proof of the lemma is concluded by the observation that as JL(a)J = R(a), a $\in$ G, we have R"(A) = φ(L"(a)) so that R"(a) = J"L"(a)J".

10. <u>Deflation</u> <u>of</u> <u>decompositions</u>. In this section we consider the problem of replacing the regular measure space (Γ , μ) which has figured in the preceding decompositions by spaces which are measure-theoretically equivalent, but which have different topological properties. Our first result asserts roughly that under appropriate, but fairly general, circumstances, (Γ , μ) may be replaced by a regular measure space (Δ , ν), which is a kind of "deflation" of (Γ , μ) which arises naturally in certain circumstances. For example, in the case of the reduction of the regular representation of a locally compact separable abelian group G, the measure ring of (Γ , μ) is identical with that of the character group G* of G under Haar measure; but Γ is topologically much "larger" than G*, roughly speaking. The general process described in the next theorem could be used to replace Γ in this situation by G*.

THEOREM 11. <u>Let $\mathcal{Q}$, $\mathcal{C}$, and z be as in Theorem 1, and suppose $\mathcal{Q}$ contains the identity operator. Let $\mathcal{E}$ be the closure in the uniform topology of the algebra generated by all functions on Γ of the form $\omega_\gamma(T)$, with T $\in \mathcal{Q}$. Let Δ be the (unique) compact Hausdorff space such that $\mathcal{E}$ is isomorphic to $C(\Delta)$, and let φ be the continuous map of Γ onto Δ such that if f $\in \mathcal{C}$, and if f corresponds to F $\in C(\Delta)$ in the isomorphism of $\mathcal{E}$ with $C(\Delta)$, then f(γ) = F($\varphi(\gamma)$) for all $\gamma \in \Gamma$. Then setting $\tau_\delta = \omega_\gamma$ when $\delta = \varphi(\gamma)$, there is a regular measure ν on Δ such that (1) $\int_\Gamma \omega_\gamma(T) d\mu(\gamma) = \int_\Delta \tau_\delta(T) d\nu(\delta)$; (2) $\delta_1 \neq \delta_2$ implies that $\tau_{\delta_1} \neq \tau_{\delta_2}$; (3) the mapping $\delta \longrightarrow \tau_\delta$ is continuous on Δ to the state space of $\mathcal{Q}$; (4) if the hypothesis of Theorem 4 is satisfied, then</u>

τ_δ is pure for almost all δ relative to (Δ, ν); (5) if $\mathcal{Q}$ is dense in C' in the weak sequential topology, then there is an algebraic isomorphism $S \longrightarrow S'(.)$ of C onto the algebra of complex-valued bounded measurable functions on (Δ, ν) such that $(STz,z) = \int_\Delta S'(\delta)\ \tau_\delta(T)\ d\nu(\delta)$ for all $S \in C$ and $T \in \mathcal{Q}$.

The existence of the Δ and φ described in the theorem is assured by known results [14]. We define ν on Borel subsets E of Δ by the equation: $\nu(E) = \mu(\varphi^{-1}(E))$; then it is readily seen that ν is a regular measure on Δ. If f is an arbitrary real-valued element of $\mathcal{E}$, then

$$\int_\Gamma f(\gamma)d\mu(\gamma) = \int_{-\infty}^\infty \lambda\, d\mu[\gamma \mid f(\gamma) < \lambda] = \int_{-\infty}^\infty \lambda\, d\nu[\delta \mid F(\delta) < \lambda],$$

where $F(\varphi(\gamma)) = f(\gamma)$, F being in $C(\Delta)$, and so $\int_\Gamma f(\gamma)d\mu(\gamma) = \int_\Delta F(\delta)d\nu(\delta)$. Now defining τ_δ as above, (1) and (3) are obvious, and (2) follows readily from the fact that $\varphi(\gamma_1) = \varphi(\gamma_2)$ if and only if $f(\gamma_1) = f(\gamma_2)$ for all $f \in \mathcal{E}$. To see (4), observe that the inverse image under φ of the Borel set $[\delta \mid \tau_\delta$ is not pure] is the set $[\gamma \mid \omega_\gamma$ is not pure], which by Theorem 4 has measure zero. To establish (5) we need the following lemma. Our method of proof here could be used to give a simple demonstration of a theorem of Dieudonné [3].

LEMMA 11.1. <u>Let (Γ, μ) be a compact perfect measure space, and $\mathcal{E}$ a uniformly closed SA subalgebra of $C(\Gamma)$ which is dense in $C(\Gamma)$ in the weak topology on $C(\Gamma)$ as the conjugate space of $L_1(\Gamma, \mu)$. Let Δ be the spectrum of $\mathcal{E}$ and let φ be a continuous map of Γ onto Δ. Then there exists a regular measure ν on Δ and an algebraic isomorphism A of $C(\Gamma)$ onto the algebra of all complex-valued bounded measurable functions on (Δ, ν) such that: (1) if $f \in \mathcal{E}$, then $(Af)(\varphi(\gamma)) = f(\gamma)$, (2) if $f \in C(\Gamma)$, then $\int f(\gamma)d\mu(\gamma) = \int(Af)(\delta)d\nu(\delta)$.</u>

Let f be arbitrary in $C(\Gamma)$. Then there exists a sequence $\{f_n\}$ in

$\mathcal{E}$ which converges weakly to f, so that in particular $\int f_n(\gamma)g(\gamma)d\mu(\gamma) \longrightarrow \int f(\gamma)g(\gamma)d\mu(\gamma)$ for $g \in \mathcal{E}$. Defining ν as above it results that $\int_\Gamma f_n(\gamma)g(\gamma)d\mu(\gamma) = \int_\Delta (A_o f_n)(\delta)(A_o g)(\delta)d\nu(\delta)$, where A_o is defined by the equation $(A_o h)(\varphi(\gamma)) = h(\gamma)$, $\gamma \in \Gamma$ for $h \in \mathcal{E}$. Now $\|f_n\|$ is necessarily bounded by a theorem about weakly convergent sequences of linear functionals on Banach spaces, and as by regularity $C(\Delta)$ is dense in $L_1(\Delta, \nu)$ it follows that $\{A_o f_n\}$ is weakly convergent in $L_\infty(\Delta, \nu)$. As this latter space is weakly sequentially complete, there exists a bounded measurable function F on Δ to which the sequence $\{A_o f_n\}$ is weakly convergent, and defining A by the equation $Af = F$, it is clear that for $f \in \mathcal{E}$, one of the values of Af is $A_o f$ and that $\int f(\gamma)g(\gamma)d\mu(\gamma) = \int (Af)(\delta)(Ag)(\delta)d\nu(\delta)$, if $f \in C(\Gamma)$ and $g \in \mathcal{E}$. Fixing f, g, and a selection of Ag, it is clear that Af is determined as an element of $L_\infty(\Delta, \nu)$, so that A is single-valued. Thus $Af = A_o f$ if $f \in \mathcal{E}$, so that (1) in the conclusion of the lemma is satisfied. It is obvious that for arbitrary $f \in C(\Gamma)$, $\int f(\gamma)d\mu(\gamma) = \int (Af)(\delta)d\nu(\delta)$.

It is easily seen that A is linear. To show that A preserves products, let f be in $C(\Gamma)$ and g in $\mathcal{E}$, and let f be the weak limit of the sequence $\{f_n\}$ in $\mathcal{E}$. Then Af is the weak limit of the sequence $\{Af_n\}$, and as multiplication is continuous in each factor separately in the weak topology, we have $fg = $ weak $\lim_n f_n g$, so $A(fg) = $ weak $\lim_n A(f_n g)$ and $A(f_n g) = A(f_n)A(g) \longrightarrow A(f)A(g)$, so that $A(fg) = A(f)A(g)$. By a repetition of the procedure just utilized, it follows that the last equation is valid for arbitrary f and g in $C(\Gamma)$. Now A is univalent, for if $Af = 0$, then from the fact that for all $g \in \mathcal{E}$, $\int f(\gamma)g(\gamma)d\mu(\gamma) = \int (Af)(\delta)(Ag)(\delta)d\nu(\delta)$, it results that $\int f(\gamma)g(\gamma)d\mu(\gamma) = 0$ for all $g \in \mathcal{E}$. From this last equation it is easy to deduce that $f = 0$.

It remains only to show that A is onto. If F is a bounded measurable function on (Δ, ν), by regularity there exists a sequence $\{F_n\}$ in $C(\Delta)$ which converges weakly to F. Now if $f_n = A^{-1}(F_n)$, from the equation $\int F_n(\delta)(Ag)(\delta)d\nu(\delta) = \int f_n(\gamma)g(\gamma)d\mu(\gamma)$ for $g \in \mathcal{C}$, it results that the sequence $\left\{\int f_n(\gamma)g(\gamma)d\mu(\gamma)\right\}$ has a limit for all $g \in \mathcal{C}$. Now $\|F_n\|$ is bounded by the theorem mentioned above, so that $\|f_n\|$ is bounded (for an algebraic isomorphism of a $C(\Gamma)$ into an algebra of essentially bounded measurable functions pre-serves norms), and it follows readily that the foregoing limit exists for all $g \in L_1(\Gamma, \mu)$. Making use again of the weak sequential complete-ness of the conjugate space of an L_1-space over a finite measure space, it results that there is an element f in $C(\Gamma)$ such that
$$\int f_n(\gamma)g(\gamma)d\mu(\gamma) \longrightarrow \int f(\gamma)g(\gamma)d\mu(\gamma) \text{ for all } g \in \mathcal{C}. \text{ Clearly}$$
$$\int(Af)(\delta)(Ag)(\delta)d\nu(\delta) = \int F(\delta)(Ag)(\delta)d\nu(\delta) \text{ for all } g \in \mathcal{C},$$
from which it is easy to conclude that $F = Af$.

The validity of conclusion (5) of the theorem follows directly from the preceding lemma together with Theorem 1.

<u>Example</u>. As an illustration of the use of the preceding result, consider the situation described in Section 8; the invariant measure m is expressed in the form $\int_\Gamma m_\gamma \, d\mu(\gamma)$, where the m_γ are ergodic in-variant measures. Taking Q, C, and z as in that section, it results that we can also write, for any continuous function f on M,
$$\int_M f(x)dm(x) = \int_\Delta \tau_\delta(Q_f)d\nu(\delta), \text{ where } Q_f \text{ is the operation of multi-}$$
plication by f, which by the same argument as in that section, leads to the equation $m(E) = \int_\Delta m'_\delta(E)d\nu(\delta)$ for any Borel set E in M. Here m'_δ is the measure associated with the state τ_δ, and is ergodic a. e. on (Δ, ν), for the inverse image of $[\delta \mid m'_\delta \text{ not ergodic}]$ is $[\gamma \mid m_\gamma \text{ not ergodic}]$, which has measure zero by Theorem 4 . We note

also that $m'_{\delta_1} \neq m'_{\delta_2}$ if $\delta_1 \neq \delta_2$.

We conclude by showing that the measure space (Γ, μ) which occurs in our decompositions can be replaced not only by any equivalent regular compact measure space, as in the preceding theorem, but, under a separability restriction, by any equivalent measure space (not necessarily bearing a topology), two measure spaces being regarded as equivalent if there is an algebraic isomorphism between their measure rings. In particular, if separable as a measure space, (Γ, μ) could be replaced by a measure space over the Borel subsets of the reals, and the decomposition of von Neumann thereby obtained.

THEOREM 12. __Let__ Q, C, __and__ z __be as in Theorem__ 1, __and suppose that__ Q __is separable__ (__in the uniform topology__) __and contains the identity operator. Let__ M = (R, $\mathcal{R}$, r) __be a measure space such that__ C __is algebraically isomorphic__ (__with preservation of adjoints__) __to the algebra of all complex-valued bounded measurable functions on__ M. __Then there exists a measure__ r' __on__ R, __an__ r-null __set__ R_o, __and a map__ p $\longrightarrow \omega_p$ __on__ $R-R_o$ __to the state space of__ A __such that:__ (1) r __and__ r' __are absolutely continuous with respect to each other__; (2) __for__ T $\in Q$, $\omega_p(T)$ __is a measurable function of__ p __on__ M; (3) __for__ T $\in Q$ __and__ S $\in C$,
$$(TSz, z) = \int_R \omega_p(T)U(p)dr'(p), \text{ __where__ } U(.) \text{ __is the function on__ } R$$
__corresponding to__ U.

Certain parts of the proof of this theorem closely resemble the proof of Theorem 1, - we shall merely sketch these portions. For any fixed T   , (STz, z) can in an obvious fashion be regarded as a continuous linear functional on $L_\infty(M)$ (in its norm topology). Moreover, if $S_n(.)$ is a sequence of elements of $L_\infty(M)$ such that $1 \geq S_n(p) \geq 0$ and $S_n(p) \geq S_{n+1}(p)$ for all n, and $\lim_n S_n(p) = 0$, all these conditions holding for almost all p   M, then $\lim F(S_n) = 0$, where we set F = F. To see this, observe that from the given algebraic isomorphism of $\mathcal{C}$ with $L_\infty(M)$ it results that if S_n is the element of $\mathcal{C}$ corresponding to $S_n(p)$, then $I \geq S_n \geq S_{n+1} \geq 0$. It is known that in this situation there exists an operator S to which the sequence $\{S_n\}$ converges strongly, so that $F_T(S_n) = (S_n Tz, z) \longrightarrow (STz, z)$. On the other hand, as an algebraic isomorphism preserves order among the self-adjoint elements, $S_n(p) \geq S(p) \geq 0$ a. e., which shows that $S(p) = 0$ a. e. and $S = 0$, so that $(STz, z) = 0$.

We next show that for any continuous linear functional Φ on $L_\infty(M)$ with the foregoing property, there exists an element $f \in L_1(M)$ such that $\Phi(k) = \int_R k(p)f(p)dr(p)$ for $k \in L_\infty(M)$. Let s be the function on R defined by the equation $s(E) = \Phi(\chi_E)$, where χ_E is the characteristic function of E ($E \in R$). Now if $E = \bigcup_i E_i$, with $E_i \in \mathcal{R}$ and the E_i mutually disjoint ($i = 1,2,\ldots$), then $\chi_E - \chi_{\bigcup_{i \leq n} E_i}$ is a sequence of functions converging monotonely to zero. So $\Phi(\chi_E - \sum_{i=1}^{n} \chi_{E_i}) \longrightarrow 0$. It follows that $s(E) = \sum_i s(E_i)$. Thus s is countably-additive; it vanishes on sets of r-measure zero; and it is bounded by $\|\Phi\|$. It results from the Radon-Nikodym theorem that $s(E) = \int_E f(p)dr(p)$ for some $f \in L_1(M)$. We have $\Phi(k) = \int_R k(p)f(p)dr(p)$ when k is a finite linear combination of characteristic functions of sets in $\mathcal{R}$. Now if k is an arbitrary non-negative-valued element of $L_\infty(M)$, there exists a sequence $\{k_n\}$ of such linear combinations such that $k_n(x)$ increases monotonely to k a. e., and with $k_n(x) \geq 0$ a. e. It follows that the same formula holds for such a k, and hence for all $k \in L_\infty(M)$.

Next we show that if f'_T is the element of $L_1(M)$ defined by the equation $(STz, z) = \int S(p)f'_T(p)dr(p)$, then $f'_I(p) \geq 0$ a. e. For if $f'_I(p) = 0$ on the set E in $\mathcal{R}$, and if S is the element of $\mathcal{C}$ corresponding to the characteristic function of E, then $(Sz, z) = 0$ clearly, but $S^2 = S$ as $(\chi_E)^2 = \chi_E$, so $(Sz, z) = \|Sz\|^2$ and $Sz = 0$.

This implies $TS_z = 0$ for $T \in \mathcal{Q}$ or $S(Tz) = 0$, from which, by the density of $\mathcal{Q}z$ in H, it follows that $S = 0$, so that E must be of measure zero. Now it is easily seen that if $\Phi(h) \geq 0$ whenever h is non-negative-valued, then the corresponding function f is a. e. non-negative-valued. Therefore $f'_I(p) \geq 0$ a. e.

This shows that r can be replaced in the integration over R by the measure r' defined by the equation $r'(E) = \int_E f'_I(p)dr(p)$, $E \in \mathcal{R}$. Let f_T now be defined for $T \in \mathcal{Q}$ by the equation $(STz, z) = \int S(p)f_T(p)dr'(p)$, $S \in C$. If $T \geq 0$, (STz, z) is a positive linear functional on C, so $f_T(p) \geq 0$ a. e. If T and U are arbitrary in $\mathcal{Q}$ and if α is an arbitrary complex number, then it is easily seen that $f_{T+U}(p) = f_T(p) + f_U(p)$ and $f_{\alpha T}(p) = \alpha f_T(p)$ a. e. We now partially normalize $f_T(p)$ by breaking $L_\infty(M)$ into equivalence classes, two (residue classes of) 'functions' (modulo the subspace of null functions) being equivalent if they are proportional (relative to constants), then selecting one 'function' from each equivalence class and then choosing any representative from the corresponding residue class, in an arbitrary fashion except for the following restrictions: 1) the representative of a 'function' which is proportional to a 'function' which is non-negative a. e. shall be everywhere proportional to a non-negative function; 2) the absolute value of the representative at any point shall not exceed the norm of the 'function' in $L_\infty(M)$; 3) the 'functions' which are zero and one a. e. shall have the representatives which are respectively everywhere zero and one; 4) a 'function' which is a. e. proportional to a real-valued function shall have a representative which is everywhere proportional to a real-valued function. It is clear that a choice of representative can be made subject to these restrictions, and that if g is any representative, assigning αg as the representative of the 'function' a. e. equal to αg yields a representative for each element of $L_\infty(M)$. We now assume that f_T is a representative, for all $T \in \mathcal{Q}$.

We have now $f_{\alpha T}(p) = \alpha f_T(p)$ and $f_{T*T}(p) \geq 0$ for all $p \in R$ and $T \in \mathcal{Q}$. Roughly speaking, it remains only to obtain a null set R_0 such that for all $p \in R-R_0$, and T and U in $\mathcal{Q}$, $f_{T+U}(p) = f_T(p) + f_U(p)$. To do this, let $\mathcal{Q}_0$ be a countable SA subring of $\mathcal{Q}$, which is dense in $\mathcal{Q}$, contains I, and which admits multiplication by rationals and by i; such a subring exists because $\mathcal{Q}$ is separable. Then the set of all pairs (U, T), with U and T in $\mathcal{Q}_0$ is countable, and hence there is a null set R_0 such that $f_{U+T}(p) = f_U(p) + f_T(p)$ for all $p \in R-R_0$ and all U and T in $\mathcal{Q}_0$. We define $\omega_p(T) = f_T(p)$ for $T \in \mathcal{Q}_0$ and $p \in R-R_0$. Now if T is arbitrary in $\mathcal{Q}$, we define $\omega_p(T)$ as follows: let $\{T_n\}$ be a sequence in $\mathcal{Q}_0$ such that $T_n \longrightarrow T$, and set $\omega_p(T) = \lim_n \omega_p(T_n)$. As $|g(p)| \leq \|g\|$ for $g \in L_\infty(M)$ by virtue of our normalization, $|\omega_p(T_n - T_m)| \leq \|T_n - T_m\|$, and clearly $\omega_p(T_n - T_m) = f_{T_n-T_m}(p) = f_{T_n}(p) - f_{T_m}(p) = \omega_p(T_n) - \omega_p(T_m)$, so the foregoing limit exists; and it is easily seen to be independent of the sequences used to approximate T, i. e., $\omega_p(T)$ is single-valued. It is readily deduced from the additivity of ω_p on $\mathcal{Q}_0$ that for arbitrary T and U in $\mathcal{Q}$, $\omega_p(U + T) = \omega_p(U) + \omega_p(T)$ for $p \notin R_0$. Now $\omega_p(T)$ is real if T is SA and $p \notin R_0$, for if $T_n \longrightarrow T$ with the T_n in $\mathcal{Q}_0$, then $T'_n = (1/2)(T_n + T_n^*) \in \mathcal{Q}_0$ and $T'_n \longrightarrow T$; and as $\omega_p(T'_n)$ is real for $p \notin R_0$, so also is $\omega_p(T)$. Moreover, $\omega_p(T*T) \geq 0$ for $T \in \mathcal{Q}$ and $p \notin R_0$, for if $T_n \longrightarrow T$ with the $T_n \in \mathcal{Q}_0$, then $T_n^*T_n \longrightarrow T*T$, and as $T_n^*T_n \in \mathcal{Q}_0$, $\omega_p(T_n^*T_n) \geq 0$.

If α is real and rational, then plainly $\omega_p(\alpha T) = \alpha \omega_p(T)$ for $T \in \mathcal{Q}_0$ and $p \notin R_0$. If α is any real number and $\{\alpha_n\}$ a sequence of rationals converging to α, then $\alpha_n T \longrightarrow \alpha T$ so that $\omega_p(\alpha_n T) \longrightarrow \omega_p(\alpha T)$ and hence $\omega_p(\alpha T) = \alpha \omega_p(T)$ for $p \notin R_0$. As $\omega_p(iT) = i\omega_p(T)$ for all p and $T \in \mathcal{Q}_0$, it follows that

$\omega_p(\alpha T) = \alpha \omega_p(T)$ for all complex α and $T \in \mathcal{Q}_o$ $(p \notin R_o)$. It is not difficult to conclude from this by the method just used that the same equation holds for all $T \in \mathcal{Q}$. It is obvious that $\omega_p(I) = 1$, and it follows from the fact that ω_p is real on SA operators that $\omega_p(T^*) = \overline{\omega}_p(T)$ for any $T \in \mathcal{Q}$. Thus ω_p is a state of $\mathcal{Q}$ $(p \notin R_o)$. To conclude the proof it is sufficient to show that $\omega_p(T) = f_T(p)$ a. e. This is true by definition for $T \in \mathcal{Q}_o$. We recall that $\|f_T\| \leq \|T\|$ for $T \in \mathcal{Q}$. Hence if $T \in \mathcal{Q}$ and if $\{T_n\}$ is a sequence in $\mathcal{Q}_o$ such that $T_n \longrightarrow T$, then $f_{T_n} \longrightarrow f_T$ in $L_\infty(M)$, and so $f_T(p)$ is a. e. the limit of $f_{T_n}(p)$. As $f_{T_n}(p) = \omega_p(T_n)$ $(p \notin R_o)$, this shows that $\omega_p(T) = f_T(p)$ a. e.

                                          I. E. Segal

REFERENCES

1.   W. Ambrose, Spectral resolution of groups of unitary operators.   Duke Mathematical Journal 11(1944) 589-595.

2.   __________, The L_2-system of a unimodular group I.   Transactions of the American Mathematical Society 65(1949) 27-48.

2a.   __________, P. R. Halmos, and S. Kakutani, The decomposition of measures.   Duke Math. Jour. 9(1942) 43-47.

3.   J. Dieudonné, Sur le theoréme de Lebesgue-Nikodym III.   Annales Univ. Grenoble, Sect. Sci. Math. et Phys. (N. S.) 23(1947-48) 25-53.

4.   I. Gelfand and D. A. Raikov, Irreducible unitary representations of locally compact groups.   Mat. Sbornik (Rec. Math.) N. S. 13(1943) 301-316 (in Russian).

4a.   R. Godement, Sur la theorie des caractères. I. Définition et classification des caractères.   C. R. Acad. Sci. Paris 229(1949) 967-69.

5.   F. Mautner, The completeness of the irreducible unitary representations of a locally compact group.   Proc. Nat. Acad. Sci. 34(1948) 52-54.

6.   __________, Unitary representations of locally compact groups.   Ann. Math. 51(1950) 1-25.

7.   F. J. Murray and J. von Neumann, On rings of operators.   Ann. Math. 37 (1936) 116-229.

8.   I. E. Segal, Irreducible representations of operator algebras.   Bull. Amer. Math. Soc. 53(1947) 73-88.

9.   __________, A class of operator algebras which are determined by groups.   Duke Math. Jour. 18(1951) 221-265.

10.   __________, The two-sided regular representation of a unimodular locally compact group.   Ann. Math. 51(1950) 293-298.

11.   __________, An extension of Plancherel's formula to separable unimodular groups.   Ann. Math. 52(1950) 272-292.

12. __________ and J. von Neumann, A theorem on unitary representations of semisimple Lie groups. Ann. Math. 52(1950) 509-517.

13. M. H. Stone, Linear transformations in Hilbert space. New York 1932.

14. __________, Application of the theory of Boolean rings to general topology. Trans. Amer. Math. Soc. 41(1937) 375-481.

15. J. von Neumann, On rings of operators. IV. Ann. Math. 41(1940) 94-161

16. __________, On rings of operators. Reduction theory. Ann. Math. 50(1949) 401-485.

17. __________, Zur algebra der funktionaloperationen und Theorie der normalen operatoren. Math. Ann. 102(1930) 370-427.

18. __________, On some algebraical properties of operator rings. Ann. Math. 44(1943) 709-715.

DECOMPOSITIONS OF OPERATOR ALGEBRAS. II:

MULTIPLICITY THEORY

by

I. E. Segal

of the

University of Chicago

1. <u>Introduction</u>. We determine the most general commutative W*-algebra (= weakly closed self-adjoint algebra of bounded linear operators on a Hilbert space) within unitary equivalence. Every such algebra is a direct sum of W*-algebras of "uniform multiplicity" and an algebra of the latter type of multiplicity n is unitarily equivalent to an n-fold copy (roughly speaking) of a maximal abelian W*-algebra. This last algebra is unitarily equivalent to the algebra of all multiplications by bounded measurable functions, of the elements in L_2 over a suitable measure space, and is determined within unitary equivalence by the Boolean ring of measurable subsets modulo the ideal of null sets in the measure space. Thus to each commutative algebra, there is for each multiplicity (cardinal number) n, a Boolean algebra B(n), and this function B determines the algebra within unitary equivalence; conversely, if B is any such function (vanishing on sufficiently large cardinals), then there exists a commutative W*-algebra whose multiplicity function is B. The classification by Maharam of Boolean measure rings shows that the measure spaces in question here can be taken to be unions of spaces measure-theoretically identical with the product measure spaces I^p, where I is the unit interval under Lebesgue measure and p is a cardinal number (with I^0 defined as a one-point space), and allows the replacement of B(n) as a complete unitary invariant by a cardinal-number-valued function $F(p, n)$ of two arbitrary cardinals giving the number of

I. E. Segal

copies of I^p whose measure ring is a constituent of B(n); and corresponding to any such function there is a commutative W*-algebra.

Similar but more limited results are obtained for W*-algebras which are not necessarily commutative. As in the commutative case, every W*-algebra is a direct sum of W*-algebras of "uniform multiplicity", and an algebra of the latter type of finite multiplicity n is unitarily equivalent to an n-fold copy of an algebra of uniform multiplicity one. When n is infinite the last conclusion is invalid except in special cases, notably in that of algebras of "type I". These are algebras which, roughly speaking, are direct integrals of factors of type I, and for them we give a complete structure theory and set of unitary invariants. Specifically, such algebras are characterized by the feature that their part of uniform multiplicity n is unitarily equivalent to an n-fold copy of a W*-algebra $\mathcal{E}_n$ of uniform multiplicity one; and are determined within unitary equivalence by the knowledge for each n of the unitary-equivalence class of the commutative algebra associated with $\mathcal{E}_n$ by virtue of the fact that the set of operators commuting with an algebra of uniform multiplicity one is commutative.

Most known results in commutative spectral theory either follow readily from the foregoing classification of commutative W*-algebras, or are seen thereby to be equivalent to questions in pure measure theory. Direct consequences of our classification (together with the known structure of separable measure spaces) include von Neumann's theorem that on a separable Hilbert space, any commutative W*-algebra consists of functions of some operator in the algebra, and the fact that such an algebra is maximal abelian if and only if it has a cyclic vector. Any commutative W*-algebra is algebraically isomorphic to a maximal abelian W*-algebra via a mapping which is weakly bicontinuous and which preserves the operational calculus. The theorem that the W*-algebra generated by a self-adjoint operator on a separable space consists of all bounded Baire functions of the operator is extended to arbitrary spaces, and a brief derivation is given of the Wecken-Plessner-Rokhlin unitary invariants of a self-adjoint operator.

Our approach has significant contacts with both the Nakano and Wecken-Plessner-Rokhlin treatments of the multiplicity theory of an individual operator, as indicated below in the specific instances. In particular, the present definition of algebra of uniform multiplicity for the commutative case is essentially due to Wecken, and the definition which we use in the not necessarily commutative case (while commutative algebras could be treated in terms of this latter definition, which we show to be equivalent to the former definition in the commutative case, it has seemed desirable in view of the central rôle of commutative algebras to treat this case separately) is a variation of that of Nakano for abelian rings of projections.

Much of the present material (notably Theorems 1-3 and 5-6) was given in a course on spectral theory at the University of Chicago in the Spring term of 1949. We are indebted to members of the course and especially to L. Nachbin for valuable criticisms and suggestions.

PART II. COMMUTATIVE ALGEBRAS

2. _Definitions_ and _technical_ _preliminaries_.

Definitions 2.1. A **W*-algebra** is a weakly closed self-adjoint algebra of (bounded linear) operators (on a Hilbert space). Thruout this paper "operator" will mean "bounded linear operator on a Hilbert space", "Hilbert space" is complex and of arbitrary dimension, and I denotes the identity operator on a Hilbert space which will be clear from the context. An algebra of operators a on a Hilbert space $\mathcal{H}$ is called an _n-fold_ _copy_ of an algebra $\mathcal{B}$ of operators on a Hilbert space $\mathcal{K}$, n being a cardinal number greater than 0, if (1) there is a set S of cardinal number n such that $\mathcal{H}$ consists of all functions f on S to K for which the series $\sum_{x \in S} ||f(x)||^2$ is convergent, with (f, g) defined as

$\sum_{x \in S} (f(x), g(x))$, and (2) $\mathcal{A}$ consists of all operators A of the form $(Af)(x) = Bf(x)$, for some B in $\mathcal{B}$. (We make the usual convention about infinite sums of complex numbers: they exist only if all but a denumerable number of terms vanish, and if the sum of this denumerable collection exists in the sense of being absolutely convergent). A __masa__ algebra of operators is one which is maximal abelian in the algebra of all operators and self-adjoint (i. e. closed under the operation of adjunction). A commutative W*-algebra $\mathcal{A} \neq 0$ is said to have __uniform multiplicity n__, where n is a cardinal number > 0, if it is unitarily equivalent to an n-fold copy of a masa algebra; the algebra consisting of the zero operator only is said to be of __uniform multiplicity zero__.

Definitions 2.2. A __measure space__ is the system composed of a set R, a ring $\mathcal{R}$ of subsets of R, and a real non-negative-valued function r on $\mathcal{R}$ such that if $\{E_i\}$ is a sequence of mutually disjoint elements of $\mathcal{R}$ for which the series $\sum_i r(E_i)$ is convergent, then $\bigcup_i E_i \in \mathcal{R}$ and $r(\bigcup_i E_i) = \sum_i r(E_i)$, and with the further property that r vanishes on the void set. If $M = (R, \mathcal{R}, r)$ is a measure space, a subset W of R is called __measurable__ if $W \cap E \in \mathcal{R}$ whenever $E \in \mathcal{R}$, and W is said to be equivalent to zero if $W \cap E$ is a null set for all $E \in \mathcal{R}$. A measure space is __localizable__ if the lattice of all measurable sets modulo the ideal of sets equivalent to zero is complete. A function on R to a topological space is called __measurable__ if the inverse image of every open set is a measurable set, and two functions are called __equivalent__ if they are equal except on a set equivalent to zero. The Banach space of all complex-valued α th-power integrable (complex-valued) functions on M (modulo the subspace of functions equivalent to zero), with the usual norm, is denoted by $L_\alpha (M)$ $(1 \leq \alpha < \infty)$; $L_\infty (M)$ is the space of bounded measurable functions, the norm of a function being defined as its essential least upper bound. The Banach algebra whose space is $L_\infty (M)$ and in which

multiplication is defined in the usual way is denoted as B(M). The algebra of all operations on L_2(M) (which denotes the usual Hilbert space, as
well as its Banach space) which consist of multiplication by an element of
B(M) is denoted by $\mathcal{M}$(M) and called the <u>multiplication algebra</u> of M.

The central results of the part of this paper which deals with
commutative algebras can now be stated.

THEOREM 1. <u>A maximal abelian self-adjoint algebra of operators
on a Hilbert space is unitarily equivalent to the algebra of all multiplications by bounded measurable functions on the Hilbert space of complex-
valued square-integrable functions over an appropriate localizable measure
space.</u>

We show in a paper [10] on measure theory to be published
separately from the present paper that two masa algebras are unitarily
equivalent if and only if they are algebraically isomorphic (in an adjoint-
preserving fashion) which in turn is true if and only if the measure rings
of the corresponding measure spaces are algebraically isomorphic. By
virtue of the Maharam classification of measure rings, the last is the case
if and only if the measure spaces have the same cardinal number invariants
naturally induced by that classification. Conversely, the multiplication
algebra of a localizable measure space is masa (in fact is masa only if the
space is localizable). We mention finally that a direct sum of finite measure spaces (see below) is always localizable.

THEOREM 2. <u>For any commutative W*-algebra</u> $\mathcal{a}$ <u>and each cardinal
number</u> $n \geq 0$ <u>there exists a projection</u> P_n <u>in</u> $\mathcal{a}$ <u>such that the least
upper bound of the</u> P_n <u>(in the lattice of projections) is the identity
operator, and with the contraction of</u> $\mathcal{a}$ <u>to the range of</u> P_n <u>of uniform
multiplicity</u> n. <u>There is a unique such function on the cardinals to the
projections in</u> $\mathcal{a}$, <u>and the</u> P_n <u>are (necessarily) mutually orthogonal.</u>

Before turning to the proof of these theorems we make some further definitions and remarks.

Definition 2.3. A measure space $(R, \mathcal{R}, r)$ is called (strictly) <u>finite</u> (in the present paper) if $R \in \mathcal{R}$. It is said to be a <u>regular</u> (locally compact) space if R is a locally compact Hausdorff space, $\mathcal{R}$ is contained in the σ-ring generated by the compact subsets of R and contains all compact subsets, and if for any $E \in \mathcal{R}$, $r(E) = \text{G.L.B.}_{W \supset E} r(W) = \text{L.U.B.}_{C \subset E} r(C)$, where W and C range respectively over the open and the compact subsets of R, which are also in $\mathcal{R}$. For any compact space Γ, $C(\Gamma)$ denotes the Banach spaces of complex-valued continuous functions on Γ, with the usual norm. A finite measure space $M = (R, \mathcal{R}, r)$ is called <u>perfect</u> if it is regular compact and if for every element of $B(M)$ there is a unique equivalent element of $C(R)$. The system constituted of a complete Boolean ring and a non-negative-valued countably-additive function on the ring is called a <u>complete measure ring</u> if every element of the ring is the least upper bound of elements of the ring on which the function is finite. If $M_\lambda = (R_\lambda, \mathcal{R}_\lambda, r_\lambda)$ are measure spaces depending on an index λ, and if the R_λ are mutually disjoint (as can be assumed without essential loss of generality), then the direct sum of the M_λ (over the index set) is the space $(R, \mathcal{R}, r)$, where $R = \bigcup_\lambda R_\lambda$, $\mathcal{R}$ is the set of all subsets E of R such that (a) E meets only (at most) countably many of the R_λ, (b) $E \cap R_\lambda \in \mathcal{R}_\lambda$ for all λ, (c) $\sum_\lambda r(E \cap R_\lambda) < \infty$, and for any such set E, $r(E) = \sum_\lambda r(E \cap R_\lambda)$.

For a discussion of many of the foregoing and related concepts, we refer to [10].

Definitions 2.4. The <u>spectrum</u> of a commutative complex Banach algebra $\mathcal{A}$ is the topological space consisting of the set of all continuous homomorphisms of $\mathcal{A}$ onto the complex numbers, topologized as a relative space of the conjugate space of $\mathcal{A}$, in its weak topology. An

"algebraic isomorphism" between two W*-algebras is a correspondence which
is an algebraic isomorphism in the usual sense, and with the further property that if two operators correspond, then so do their adjoints. (In
other words, we take the "algebra" of a W*-algebra to be an algebra with a
distinguished involutory antiautomorphism, viz. that of adjunction).

An element z of a Hilbert space $\mathcal{H}$ is called a <u>cyclic vector</u>
for a set $\mathcal{S}$ of operators on $\mathcal{H}$ if the set of all Sz, with $S \in \mathcal{S}$,
spans $\mathcal{H}$ (i. e. $\mathcal{H}$ is the smallest closed linear manifold containing
those elements). If $\mathcal{M}$ is a closed linear subspace of $\mathcal{H}$ which is invariant under $\mathcal{S}$, z is called a <u>relative cyclic vector</u> when the Sz,
$S \in \mathcal{S}$, span $\mathcal{M}$. The <u>contraction of</u> $\mathcal{S}$ <u>to</u> $\mathcal{M}$, denoted as $\mathcal{S}_M$, is the
collection of all operators on $\mathcal{M}$ of the form $x \longrightarrow Sx$, with $S \in \mathcal{S}$
($x \in \mathcal{M}$). The set of all operators on $\mathcal{H}$ which commute with each element
of $\mathcal{S}$ is called the <u>commutor</u> of $\mathcal{S}$ and denoted $\mathcal{S}'$.

If T is a SA (self-adjoint) operator on a Hilbert space $\mathcal{H}$
with corresponding resolution of the identity $\{E_\lambda\}$ (so that T
$=\int \lambda dE_\lambda$), the <u>spectral measure associated with</u> T is the function $E(.)$
on the Borel subsets of the reals to the projections on $\mathcal{H}$ determined by
the condition that it be countably-additive, regular, and that if B is
the closed interval $(-\infty, \lambda]$, then $E(B) = E_\lambda$. If P_μ is any family
of projections on $\mathcal{H}$ indexed by μ , then $\bigcup_\mu P_\mu$ denotes the least
upper bound and $\bigcap_\mu P_\mu$ the greatest lower bound of the P_μ in the
lattice of all projections on $\mathcal{H}$.

3. <u>Structure of maximal abelian W*-algebras</u>. We prove Theorem 1
in this section and obtain some incidental results which may be noteworthy.
In particular, it is clear from the proof that the measure space in question in that theorem can be taken to be a direct sum of finite perfect
spaces.

LEMMA 1.1. <u>If $\mathcal{A}$ is a SA algebra of operators on a Hilbert space $\mathcal{H}$, then $\mathcal{H}$ is a discrete direct sum of subspaces each of which is invariant under $\mathcal{A}$ and has a relative cyclic vector for $\mathcal{A}$.</u>

It is clear from Zorn's formulation of transfinite induction that there exists a collection $\overline{\Xi}$ of mutually orthogonal closed linear subspaces of $\mathcal{H}$, each of which is invariant under $\mathcal{A}$ and has a relative cyclic vector for $\mathcal{A}$, and which is maximal with respect to these properties. If $\mathcal{K}$ is the discrete direct sum of the elements of $\overline{\Xi}$, then $\mathcal{K} = \mathcal{H}$, for if x is a nonzero element of the orthogonal complement of $\mathcal{K}$ in $\mathcal{H}$, the closure of $\mathcal{A}x$ is easily seen to be invariant under $\mathcal{A}$, to have the relative cyclic vector x, and to be orthogonal to all the elements of $\overline{\Xi}$.

LEMMA 1.2. <u>A commutative W*-algebra with a cyclic vector is unitarily equivalent to the algebra of all multiplications by bounded measurable functions on L_2 over a finite perfect measure space.</u>

Let $\mathcal{A}$ be a W*-algebra on $\mathcal{H}$ with cyclic vector z. It follows from any of a number of representation theorems (see e. g. [11], Th. 1) that $\mathcal{A}$ is isomorphic as a Banach algebra to $C(\Gamma)$, where Γ is the spectrum of $\mathcal{A}$. For $T \in \mathcal{A}$, let $T(.)$ denote the corresponding function on Γ. Let ω be the functional on $\mathcal{A}$ defined by the equation $\omega(T) = (Tz, z)$, $T \in \mathcal{A}$, and let ω' be the naturally induced functional on $C(\Gamma)$, so that $\omega'(T(.)) = \omega(T)$. Then by the Riesz-Markoff theorem there is a unique regular measure μ on Γ such that $\omega'(T(.)) = \int_{\Gamma} T(\gamma)d\mu(\gamma)$, $T \in \mathcal{A}$. It follows from [9], Theorem 1, that (Γ, μ) is a perfect measure space.

Now let U_0 be the function on $\mathcal{A}z$ to $L_2(\Gamma, \mu)$ defined as follows: $U_0(Tz) = T(.)$, - $T(.)$ is a continuous function on the finite regular compact measure space (Γ, μ), and hence square-integrable. Now U_0 preserves norms, for $||Tz||^2 = (Tz, Tz) = (T^*Tz, z) = \omega(T^*T)$ $= \int_\Gamma (T^*T)(\gamma)d\mu(\gamma) = \int_\Gamma |T(\gamma)|^2 d\mu(\gamma)$. This shows that U_0 is single-valued, for if $Sz = Tz$ with S and T in $\mathcal{Q}$, then $(S-T)z =0$, and so $(S-T)(.) = 0$ in $L_2(\Gamma, \mu)$, i. e. $S(\gamma) - T(\gamma) = 0$ a. e., or $S(\gamma) = T(\gamma)$ a. e. As $\mathcal{Q}z$ is dense in $\mathcal{H}$, and by regularity $C(\Gamma)$ is (subject to an obvious identification) dense in $L_2(\Gamma, \mu)$, U_0 can be uniquely extended to a unitary transformation U on $\mathcal{H}$ to $L_2(\Gamma, \mu)$.

We show next that U takes $\mathcal{Q}$ onto $\mathcal{M}(\Gamma, \mu)$, the multiplication algebra of (Γ, μ). This means that the map $T \rightarrow UTU^{-1}$ on $\mathcal{Q}$ will be shown to be onto $\mathcal{M}(\Gamma, \mu)$. We show actually that $UTU^{-1} = M_T$, where M_T is the operation of multiplication of elements of $L_2(\Gamma, \mu)$ by $T(.)$. The onto character of the map is then an immediate consequence of the fact that (Γ, μ) is perfect. Now as UTU^{-1} and M_T are both bounded operators on $L_2(\Gamma, \mu)$, it suffices to show that $UTU^{-1}x = M_Tx$ for x ranging over a dense subset of $L_2(\Gamma, \mu)$, e. g., over $C(\Gamma)$. Now if $x \in C(\Gamma)$, then $x = S(.)$ for some $S \in \mathcal{Q}$ and $U^{-1}x = Sz$, so $UTU^{-1}x = (TS)(.)$. Obviously $M_Tx = T(.)S(.)$, which equals $(TS)(.)$ as the map $T \rightarrow T(.)$ is an algebraic isomorphism.

COROLLARY 1.1. <u>A commutative W*-algebra which has a cyclic vector is maximal abelian.</u>

For the multiplication algebra of a finite measure space is maximal abelian (see e.g. [10]).

PROOF OF THEOREM. Let $\mathcal{Q}$ be a masa algebra on $\mathcal{H}$, and let $\mathcal{H}$ be the direct sum of the closed linear subspaces $\mathcal{H}_\xi$, $\xi \in \Xi$, each of which is invariant under $\mathcal{Q}$ and has a cyclic vector for $\mathcal{Q}$, - these exist by Lemma 1.1. The contraction of $\mathcal{Q}$ to $\mathcal{H}_\xi$ is by Lemma 1.2 unitarily equivalent, say via the unitary transformation U_ξ , to the multiplication algebra of the finite perfect measure space $M_\xi = (\Gamma_\xi , \mu_\xi)$, and it is clearly no loss of generality to take $\Gamma_\xi \cap \Gamma_{\xi'} = 0$ for $\xi \neq \xi'$. Now let $M = (R, \mathcal{R}, r)$ be the direct sum of the M_ξ , $\xi \in \Xi$. We define a unitary transformation U on $\mathcal{H}$ to $L_2(M)$ as follows: if $x \in \mathcal{H}$, let $x = \sum_{\xi \in \Xi} x_\xi$ with $x_\xi \in H_\xi$, and set $Ux = \sum_{\xi \in \Xi} U_\xi x_\xi$ (this sum exists in the sense of unconditional convergence for the $U_\xi x_\xi$ are mutually orthogonal and $\sum_\xi \| U_\xi x_\xi \|^2 = \sum_\xi \| x_\xi \|^2 = \| x \|^2$). It is easily verified that U is, actually, unitary.

It remains only to show that the map on the operators in $\mathcal{Q}$ to those on $L_2(M)$ takes $\mathcal{Q}$ onto $\mathcal{M}(M)$, i. e. that $\mathcal{M}(M) = U \mathcal{Q} U^{-1}$. Let T be arbitrary in $\mathcal{Q}$, let T_ξ be the contraction of T to $\mathcal{H}_\xi$, and let t be the function on R defined as follows: if $p \in \Gamma_\xi$, then $t(p) = T_\xi(p)$ (where $T_\xi(.)$ is the bounded measurable function on Γ_ξ corresponding to T, i. e., $U_\xi T_\xi U_\xi^{-1}$ is the operation of multiplication by $T_\xi(.)$). It is easily seen that $t(.)$ is measurable on M, and $\| t(.) \|_\infty \leq \text{L.U.B.}_{\xi \in \Xi} \| T_\xi(.) \|$. Now the bound of the operation of multiplication by a bounded measurable function on a measure space, of elements of L_2 over the space, is readily seen to be identical with the bound of the function in L_∞ Hence $\| T_\xi(.) \| \leq \| U_\xi T_\xi U_\xi^{-1} \| = \| T_\xi \| \leq \| T \|$, so that t is bounded. To show that UTU^{-1} is the operation Q_t of multiplication by t it is enough, in view of the boundedness of these operators, to show that they agree on a dense subset of $L_2(M)$. In particular it suffices to show that $UTU^{-1}f = Q_t f$ if f vanishes outside of a finite union of the Γ_ξ and coincides on each with a continuous function. The foregoing equation is linear in f, and so it is sufficient even to show that $UTU^{-1}f = Q_t f$ for f vanishing outside of Γ_ξ and continuous on Γ_ξ ($\xi \in \Xi$). But for such an f, $(Q_t f)(x) = t'_\xi(x)f(x)$, where $t'_\xi(x) = T_\xi(x)$ for $x \in \Gamma_\xi$ and $t'_\xi(x) = 0$ otherwise; while $(UTU^{-1}f)(x) = (UTU_\xi^{-1}f)(x)$ (as U^{-1} coincides with U_ξ^{-1} on $U\mathcal{H}_\xi$) $= (U_\xi TU_\xi^{-1}f)(x)$ (for $U_\xi^{-1}f \in \mathcal{H}_\xi$, T leaves $\mathcal{H}_\xi$ invariant, and U agrees with U_ξ on $\mathcal{H}_\xi$), $= T_\xi(x)f(x)$ for $x \in \Gamma_\xi$ and vanishes for $x \in \Gamma_\xi$ (by the definition of U_ξ), and so finally is equal to $t'_\xi(x)f(x)$ also.

At this point we use, for the first time in the proof, the assumption that $\mathcal{A}$ is masa. It follows that UQU^{-1} is likewise masa. As $U\mathcal{A}U^{-1}$ has been shown to be contained in $\mathcal{M}(M)$, and as the latter algebra is obviously abelian and SA, it results that $U\mathcal{A}U^{-1} \supset \mathcal{M}(M)$, and hence that $U\mathcal{A}U^{-1} = \mathcal{M}(M)$.

COROLLARY 1.2. <u>A maximal abelian self-adjoint algebra of operators on a separable Hilbert space has a cyclic vector.</u>

By the known classification of separable measure spaces, every such space has its measure ring isomorphic to that of a finite measure space. Now it is clear that if L_2 over a measure space is separable, then so is the measure space, and hence a masa algebra $\mathcal{M}$ on a separable Hilbert space $\mathcal{H}$ is unitarily equivalent to the multiplication algebra of a finite measure space. It is clear that the function identically unity is a cyclic vector for the multiplication algebra of a finite measure space, and hence the corresponding vector in $\mathcal{H}$ is cyclic for $\mathcal{M}$.

We remark that the present corollary follows also without the use of the classification theorem for separable measure spaces, from the observation that any collection of mutually orthogonal projections on a separable Hilbert space is at most countable, together with Lemma 2.5 and the remark in the proof of Lemma 2.9 to the effect that a separating vector for a masa algebra is cyclic (the proofs both of the lemma and the remark being independent of the corollary).

Remark 3.1. The result established in this section essentially
includes the spectral theorem, and can be used as a basis for the operational calculus. The fact that a commutative W*-algebra is algebraically isomorphic to a $C(\Gamma)$ is nearly equivalent to the spectral theorem, and the
theorem follows readily in full from Theorem 1. We illustrate the situation by considering the case of a SA operator T on a Hilbert space $\mathcal{H}$,
the same procedure being valid for any finite number of commuting SA operators.

By transfinite induction there exists a masa algebra $\mathcal{M}$ containing T, and it follows from Theorem 1 that $\mathcal{M}$ is unitarily equivalent to
the multiplication algebra of a localizable measure space $M = (R, \mathcal{R}, r)$.
Let T correspond to the operation T' of multiplication by the real-
valued bounded measurable function k, let $S_\lambda = \left[p \in R \mid k(p) \leq \lambda \right]$,
let E'_λ be the operation of multiplication by the characteristic function
of S_λ , and let E_λ be the operator in M corresponding to E'_λ . It is
a straightforward application of known measure theory to verify that T'
$= \int \lambda dE'_\lambda$ in the usual sense (that $(T'f, g) = \int_{-\infty}^{\infty} \lambda \, d(E'_\lambda f, g)$ for any
f and g in $L_2(M)$), and that $\text{strong lim}_{\varepsilon \longrightarrow +0} E_{\lambda+\varepsilon} = E_\lambda$. It
follows that $T = \int \lambda dE_\lambda$, where $\{E_\lambda\}$ is a resolution of the iden-
tity in the usual sense, and it is readily seen that E_λ commutes with
all operators which commute with T, and that the family $\{E_\lambda\}$ is
unique.

Now let ψ be any bounded Baire function on the reals. We shall
show that $\psi(T)$ can be defined simply as the operator in $\mathcal{M}$ corresponding to the operation of multiplication by $\psi(k(p))$. Again measure theory
of a standard sort implies that this operation is $\int \psi(\lambda) dE'_\lambda$, and it
follows that the corresponding operator in $\mathcal{M}$ is $\int \psi(\lambda) dE_\lambda$, and so in
particular is independent of the masa algebra in which T is imbedded.

4. <u>Structure of commutative W*-algebras</u>. We base the proof of Theorem 2 on a series of lemmas.

LEMMA 2.1. <u>Let</u> $\mathcal{A}$ <u>be a commutative W*-algebra of uniform multiplicity</u> n, <u>on a Hilbert space</u> $\mathcal{H}$. <u>If</u> P <u>is a nonzero projection in</u> $\mathcal{A}$, <u>then the contraction of</u> $\mathcal{A}$ <u>to the range of</u> P <u>likewise has uniform multiplicity</u> n.

In proving this, there is evidently no loss of generality in taking $\mathcal{A}$ to be an n-fold copy of the masa algebra $\mathcal{M}$ on $\mathcal{K}$ (rather than unitarily equivalent to such a copy), so that $\mathcal{H}$ consists of all functions f on a set S, of cardinal number n, to $\mathcal{K}$, for which the sum $\sum_{x \in S} \|f(x)\|^2$ is convergent, and $(f, g) = \sum_{x \in S} (f(x), g(x))$ for f and g in $\mathcal{H}$; and $\mathcal{A}$ consists of all operators of the form $(Af)(x) = Bf(x)$, with $B \in \mathcal{M}$. For $B \in \mathcal{M}$, let $\varphi(B)$ be the operator in $\mathcal{A}$ defined by the preceding equation. It is clear that φ is an algebraic isomorphism of $\mathcal{M}$ onto $\mathcal{A}$, and hence there is a projection $\tilde{P}$ in $\mathcal{M}$ such that $\varphi(\tilde{P}) = P$. Putting $\mathcal{K}_1$ for the range of $\tilde{P}$, $\mathcal{M}_1$ for the contraction of $\mathcal{M}$ to $\mathcal{K}_1$, and $\mathcal{A}_1$ for the contraction of $\mathcal{A}$ to the range of P, it is not difficult to verify that $\mathcal{A}_1$ is an n-fold copy of $\mathcal{M}_1$ on $\mathcal{K}_1$. It follows that it is sufficient to prove the lemma for the case n = 1.

Now assuming n = 1, it must be shown that if $\tilde{W}$ is in the commutor of $\mathcal{A}_1$, then $\tilde{W} \in \mathcal{A}_1$ (it is clear that $\mathcal{A}_1$ is SA). Let W be the operator on $\mathcal{H}$ defined by the equation $Wx = \tilde{W}Px$, $x \in \mathcal{H}$. Then $W \in \mathcal{A}'$, for if T and x are arbitrary in $\mathcal{A}$ and $\mathcal{H}$ respectively, $WTx = \tilde{W}PTx = \tilde{W}PTPx$ (for $\mathcal{A}$ is abelian) $= \tilde{W}\tilde{T}Px$ (where $\tilde{T}$ is the contraction of T to $P\mathcal{H}$) $= \tilde{T}\tilde{W}Px$ (since $\tilde{W} \in (\mathcal{A}_1)'$) $=$ $\tilde{T}P\tilde{W}Px$ (as $\tilde{W}Px \in P\mathcal{H}$) $= TP\tilde{W}Px$ (by the definition of $\tilde{T}$) $= T\tilde{W}Px$ (since $\tilde{W}Px \in P\mathcal{H}$) $= TWx$. Hence $W \in \mathcal{A}$, and it follows that the contraction of W to $P\mathcal{H}$ is in $\mathcal{A}_1$, and this contraction is $\tilde{W}$.

LEMMA 2.2. Let $\mathcal{M}_\mu$ be a masa algebra on the Hilbert space $\mathcal{K}_\mu$, where μ ranges over an index set, and let $\mathcal{K}$ be the direct sum of the $\mathcal{K}_\mu$. Let $\mathcal{M}$ be the set of all operators T on $\mathcal{K}$ determined by such an equation as $Tx = \sum_\mu T_\mu P_\mu x$, where $x \in \mathcal{K}$, P_μ is the projection of $\mathcal{K}$ onto $\mathcal{K}_\mu$, $T_\mu \in \mathcal{M}_\mu$, and with $\|T_\mu\|$ bounded. Then $\mathcal{M}$ is a masa algebra.

In the statement of this lemma, and elsewhere when convenient, we make the obvious identification of a summand in a direct sum of Hilbert spaces with a closed linear manifold in the sum. It is readily verified that the algebra $\mathcal{M}$ defined in the lemma is SA. To prove the lemma we need therefore only show that if $W \in \mathcal{M}'$, then $W \in \mathcal{M}$. From the definition of $\mathcal{M}$ it is clear that $P_\mu \in \mathcal{M}$, so that P_μ and W commute, which implies that W leaves invariant the subspace $P_\mu \mathcal{H} = \mathcal{K}_\mu$. Now the operation of contracting an operator to an invariant closed linear manifold is a homomorphism of the algebra of all operators leaving the manifold invariant, into the algebra of operators on the manifold. Hence the contraction W_μ of W to $\mathcal{K}_\mu$ commutes with the contraction to the same manifold of each element of $\mathcal{M}$, and so commutes with every operator in $\mathcal{M}_\mu$. As $\mathcal{M}_\mu$ is maximal abelian, it results that $W_\mu \in \mathcal{M}_\mu$. Now $\|W_\mu\| = \|P_\mu W\| \leq \|W\|$, so that $\|W_\mu\|$ is bounded, and it follows that $W \in \mathcal{M}$.

LEMMA 2.3. If $\{P_\mu\}$ is a family of mutually orthogonal projections in the commutative W*-algebra $\mathcal{A}$, and if the contraction of $\mathcal{A}$ to $P_\mu \mathcal{H}$ has uniform multiplicity n for all μ, then the contraction $\mathcal{A}_0$ of $\mathcal{A}$ to $(\bigcup_\mu P_\mu)\mathcal{H}$ likewise has uniform multiplicity n.

Let the contraction $\mathcal{A}_\mu$ of $\mathcal{A}$ to $P_\mu \mathcal{H}$ be unitarily equivalent, via the unitary transformation U_μ on $P_\mu \mathcal{H}$, to an n-fold copy, say C_μ on $\mathcal{L}_\mu$, of the masa algebra $\mathcal{M}_\mu$ on $\mathcal{K}_\mu$. If S_μ is the set which here plays the role of the set S in Definition 2.1, all the S_μ have cardinal number n, and it is clearly no essential loss of generality to take all the S_μ to be identical and equal, say, to S. Let $\mathcal{K}$ be the direct sum of the $\mathcal{K}_\mu$, and let $\mathcal{M}$ be the set of all operators T on $\mathcal{K}$ of the form $Tx = \sum_\mu T_\mu R_\mu x$, $x \in \mathcal{K}$, where R_μ is the projection of $\mathcal{K}$ onto $\mathcal{K}_\mu$, $T_\mu \in \mathcal{M}_\mu$, and such that $\|T_\mu\|$ is bounded. By the preceding lemma $\mathcal{M}$ masa, and the remainder of the proof consists in showing that a_0 is unitarily equivalent to an n-fold copy of $\mathcal{M}$ on $\mathcal{K}$.

We first define a unitary transformation U on $\mathcal{H}' = (\bigcup_\mu P_\mu)\mathcal{H}$ to the n-fold direct sum $\mathcal{L}$ of $\mathcal{K}$ with itself. For any $x \in \mathcal{H}$, $U_\mu P_\mu x$ is some element of $\mathcal{L}_\mu$, say $f_\mu(.)$, and $\|P_\mu x\|^2 = \|U_\mu P_\mu x\|^2 = \sum_{a \in S} \|f_\mu(a)\|^2$. Now $\|x\|^2 = \sum_\mu \|P_\mu x\|^2$, so that the series $\sum_\mu (\sum_{a \in S} \|f_\mu(a)\|^2)$ is convergent, and it follows that the series $\sum_{a \in S} \sum_\mu \|f_\mu(a)\|^2$ is also convergent. Now $f_\mu(a) \in \mathcal{K}_\mu$ and the $\mathcal{K}_\mu$ are mutually orthogonal subspaces of $\mathcal{K}$, so that the convergence of $\sum_\mu \|f_\mu(a)\|^2$ implies the convergence of $\sum_\mu f_\mu(a)$ to an element $f(a)$ of $\mathcal{K}$, where $\|f(a)\|^2 = \sum_\mu \|f_\mu(a)\|^2$. As $\sum_{a \in S} \|f(a)\|^2 = \sum_a \sum_\mu \|f_\mu(a)\|^2$, which last expression is a convergent series, we have $f \in \mathcal{L}$. We define U by the equation $Ux = f$ and observe that U is linear and isometric. To show that U is unitary it remains only to show that it is onto $\mathcal{L}$. Now let g be arbitrary in $\mathcal{L}$, and let g_μ be defined by the equation $g_\mu(a) = R_\mu g(a)$. Then $\sum_a \|g_\mu(a)\|^2 \leq \sum_a \|g(a)\|^2$ so that $g_\mu \in \mathcal{L}_\mu$, and as $\sum R_\mu x = x$ for all x in $\mathcal{K}$, we have $g = \sum_\mu g_\mu$. Let $y_\mu = U_\mu^{-1} g_\mu$ and set $y = \sum_\mu y_\mu$; as the y_μ are in $P_\mu \mathcal{H}$, they are mutually orthogonal, and the sum $\sum_\mu \|y_\mu\|^2$ is absolutely convergent as $\|y_\mu\| = \|g_\mu\|$, so that the sum defining y is unconditionally convergent. By the definition of U, $(Uy)(a) = \sum_\mu (U_\mu P_\mu y)(a) = \sum_\mu (U_\mu y_\mu)(a) = \sum_\mu g_\mu(a) = \sum_\mu R_\mu g(a) = g(a)$, so $Uy = g$.

Finally we show that $UA_o U^{-1}$ is an n-fold copy of $\mathcal{M}$ on $\mathcal{K}$. We first observe that by the preceding paragraph, $\mathcal{L}$ is the direct sum of the $\mathcal{L}_\mu$. Now let T be arbitrary in $\mathcal{Q}_o$, let T_μ be the contraction of T to $P_\mu \mathcal{H}$, and let $\tilde{T}_\mu$ be the operator $U_\mu T_\mu U_\mu^{-1}$ on $\mathcal{L}_\mu$. Then $\| \tilde{T}_\mu \| = \| T_\mu \| \leq \| T \|$, and as the $\mathcal{L}_\mu$ are mutually orthogonal, there exists a unique operator $\tilde{T}$ on $\mathcal{L}$ which is an extension of all the $\tilde{T}_\mu$. By the definition of U_μ, $\tilde{T}_\mu \in \mathcal{C}_\mu$, and putting φ_μ for the map on $\mathcal{M}_\mu$ to $\mathcal{C}_\mu$ defined by the equation $(\varphi_\mu (W')f_\mu)(a) = W'f_\mu(a)$, $W' \in \mathcal{M}_\mu$, $f_\mu(a) \in \mathcal{K}_\mu$, we set $T'_\mu = \varphi_\mu^{-1}(\tilde{T}_\mu)$, and put T' for the operator on $\mathcal{K}$ determined by the equation $T'x = \sum_\mu T'_\mu R_\mu x$, $x \in \mathcal{K}$. As φ_μ is easily seen to preserve the bounds of operators, $\| T_\mu \|$ is bounded and so T' exists and is in $\mathcal{M}$.

We show now that $UTU^{-1} = \varphi(T')$, where φ is the map on $\mathcal{M}$ to the operators on $\mathcal{L}$ given by the equation $(\varphi(W')f)(a) = W'f(a)$, $f \in \mathcal{L}$. As the $\mathcal{L}_\mu$ span $\mathcal{L}$, and as both UTU^{-1} and $\varphi(T')$ are bounded, it suffices to show that $UTU^{-1}f_\mu = \varphi(T')f_\mu$ for all $f_\mu \in \mathcal{L}_\mu$. Now $(\varphi(T')f_\mu)(a) = T'f_\mu(a) = T'_\mu f_\mu(a)$. On the other hand, $(UTU^{-1}f_\mu)(a) = (U_\mu T_\mu U_\mu^{-1}f_\mu)(a) = (\tilde{T}_\mu f_\mu)(a) = (T'_\mu f_\mu)(a)$. It remains only to show that every element of $\mathcal{M}$ has the form $\varphi^{-1}(UTU^{-1})$ for some $T \in \mathcal{Q}_o$. Let T' be an arbitrary element of $\mathcal{M}$ and let T_μ be the contraction of T' to $\mathcal{K}_\mu$. Let $T_\mu = U_\mu^{-1} \varphi_\mu(T'_\mu)U_\mu$, so that T_μ is an operator on $P_\mu \mathcal{H}$ in A_μ, and let $\hat{T}_\mu$ be the (unique) operator on $\mathcal{H}$ which agrees with T_μ on $P_\mu \mathcal{H}$, and which annihilates the orthogonal complement of $P_\mu \mathcal{H}$. Now T_μ is the contraction of some element A of $\mathcal{Q}$ to $P_\mu \mathcal{H}$, and clearly $P_\mu AP_\mu = \hat{T}_\mu$, so $\hat{T}_\mu \in \mathcal{Q}$. As $\| \hat{T}_\mu \| = \| T_\mu \| = \| \varphi_\mu(T'_\mu) \| = \| T'_\mu \| \leq \| T' \|$, the directed set

$\sum_{\mu \in F} \hat{T}_{\mu}$, where F ranges over the finite subsets of the μ's (ordered by inclusion) converges strongly to an operator T on $\mathcal{H}$. Obviously $T \in \mathcal{A}$, and it is straightforward to verify that $UTU^{-1} = \varphi(T')$.

LEMMA 2.4. _If_ $\mathcal{A}$ _is a commutative W*-algebra on_ $\mathcal{H}$ _and if_ $\{P_{\mu}\}$ _is a family of projections in_ $\mathcal{A}$ _such that the contraction of_ $\mathcal{A}$ _to_ $P_{\mu}\mathcal{H}$ _is of uniform multiplicity_ n _for each_ μ , _then the contraction of_ $\mathcal{A}$ _to_ $(\bigcup_{\mu} P_{\mu})\mathcal{H}$ _is likewise of uniform multiplicity_ n.

It is no loss of generality to assume that the index set over which μ varies is well-ordered. Setting $Q_{\mu} = P_{\mu}(I - \bigcup_{\nu < \mu} P_{\nu})$, then $Q_{\mu} \in \mathcal{A}$ (as the projections in a W*-algebra constitute a complete lattice, which is a Boolean algebra when the W*-algebra is commutative), and as the contraction of $\mathcal{A}$ to $P_{\mu}\mathcal{H}$ is of uniform multiplicity n, it follows from Lemma 2.1 that the contraction of $\mathcal{A}$ to $Q_{\mu}P_{\mu}\mathcal{H} = Q_{\mu}\mathcal{H}$ is also of uniform multiplicity n (assigning all multiplicities to an algebra of operators on a zero-dimensional space). It is readily verified that the Q_{μ} are mutually orthogonal, and hence the preceding lemma implies that the contraction of $\mathcal{A}$ to $(\bigcup_{\mu} Q_{\mu})\mathcal{H}$ is of uniform multiplicity n. Finally, it is not difficult to verify that $\bigcup_{\mu} Q_{\mu} = \bigcup_{\mu} P_{\mu}$.

The concepts described in the following definition are among those used by Nakano in [7] , and the next lemma is due to Nakano; the proof which we give of its non-trivial half is somewhat simpler that that which Nakano indicates.

Definitions 4.1. A W*-algebra $\mathcal{A}$ on $\mathcal{H}$ is called countably-decomposable if every family of mutually orthogonal non-zero projections in $\mathcal{A}$ is at most countable. An element x in $\mathcal{H}$ is called a separating vector for $\mathcal{A}$ if the only projection P in $\mathcal{A}$ for which Px = 0 is the zero projection; if R is a projection in $\mathcal{A}'$, x is called a relative

18　　　　　　　　　　　　　　　　　I. E. Segal

separating <u>vector</u> (for Q on $R\mathcal{H}$) if $x \in R\mathcal{H}$ and x is a separating vector for the contraction of Q to $R\mathcal{H}$.

Remark 4.1. If an element x is a separating vector for Q, then the equation $Tx = 0$, $T \in Q$, implies that $T = 0$. For if $Tx = 0$, then $(T*T)x = 0$, and it follows that if W is any operator in the W*-algebra C generated by $T*T$, then $Wx = 0$. As x is a separating vector for Q, which contains C, C can contain no nonzero projection. Now any W*-algebra is generated by the projections it contains, so $C = (0)$, which means $T*T = 0$ and so finally $T = 0$.

LEMMA 2.5. <u>A commutative W*-algebra is countably decomposable if and only if it has a separating vector.</u>

If Q is a commutative W*-algebra on $\mathcal{H}$ with a separating vector x, then Q is countably decomposable, for if $\{P_\mu\}$ is any family of mutually orthogonal projections in Q, then $\|x\|^2 \geq \sum_\mu \|P_\mu x\|^2$, so that all but at most countably many of the $P_\mu x$ are zero, which implies that all but at most countably many of the P_μ are zero.

Now let Q be a countably-decomposable commutative W*-algebra on $\mathcal{H}$, and let $\mathcal{F}$ be a family of projections in Q which is maximal with respect to the properties: 1) Q has a relative separating vector on $P\mathcal{H}$, for $P \in \mathcal{F}$; 2) the elements of $\mathcal{F}$ are mutually orthogonal. Evidently $\mathcal{F}$ is at most countable: let its elements be $\{P_i; i = 1,2,...\}$ and let x_i be a relative separating vector of unit norm for Q on $P_i\mathcal{H}$. It is easily verified that $y = \sum_i 2^{-i}x_i$ is then a relative separating vector of Q on $(\bigcup_i P_i)\mathcal{H}$. Now $\bigcup_i P_i = I$, for otherwise there exists a nonzero element z in $(I - \bigcup_i P_i)\mathcal{H}$ and if Q_0 is the least upper bound of the projections Q in Q which are bounded by $I - \bigcup_i P_i$ and for which $Qz = 0$, then Q has the relative separating vector z on

$(I - \bigcup_i P_i - Q_0)H$ and $I - \bigcup_i P_i - Q_0$ is orthogonal to all the P_i, which by the fact that $Q_0 \neq 0$ contradicts the maximality of $\mathcal{F}$. Hence y is a separating vector for Q on H.

LEMMA 2.6. *If* Q *is a* commutative *nonzero* countably-decomposable *W*-algebra on* H, *then* there exists a nonzero projection P in Q such that the contraction of Q to PH has uniform multiplicity.

Let $\mathcal{S}$ be a set of separating vectors for Q which is maximal with respect to the property that if x and y are any two elements of $\mathcal{S}$, then Qx is orthogonal to Qy. Put $\mathcal{K}_x$ for the closure of Qx and P_x for the projection of H onto $\mathcal{K}_x$. Let Q_0 be the least upper bound of the projections Q in Q for which $Q(I - \bigcup_x P_x) = 0$, and let $\mathcal{L}$ be the closed linear subspace of H spanned by the $\mathcal{K}_x$. Then $Q_0 \neq 0$, for if $Q_0 = 0$, then $I - \bigcup_x P_x \neq 0$ and the contraction of Q to $(I - \bigcup_x P_x)H = H \ominus \mathcal{L}$ is an isomorphism, by the proof of Remark 4.1, and putting z for any relative separating vector for Q on $H \ominus \mathcal{L}$ (which exists by Lemma 2.5), then z is a separating vector for Q such that Qz is orthogonal to all the Qx with $x \in \mathcal{S}$, - which contradicts the maximality of $\mathcal{S}$.

Clearly $Q_0 = \bigcup_x Q_0 P_x$, and putting $P'_x = Q_0 P_x$ and $\mathcal{K}'_x$ for the range of P'_x, the contraction Q_x of Q to $\mathcal{K}'_x$ has the relative separating vector $Q_0 x$, and is algebraically isomorphic to the contraction of Q to $Q_0 H$. By Corollary 1.1, Q_x is masa. Now we utilize a result in $[10]$: if two masa algebras are algebraically isomorphic, then they are unitarily equivalent. It follows that there exists a masa algebra $\mathcal{M}$ on a Hilbert space $\mathcal{K}'$ such that for each $x \in \mathcal{S}$, Q_x on $P'_x H$ is unitarily equivalent to $\mathcal{M}$ on $\mathcal{K}'$. Now the direct sum of the $P'_x H$ is $Q_0 H$, and it follows without difficulty by a technique previously employed that if n is the cardinal number of $\mathcal{S}$, then the contraction of Q to

$Q_o \mathcal{H}$ is unitarily equivalent to an n-fold copy of $\mathcal{M}$ on $\mathcal{K}'$.

LEMMA 2.7. If $\mathcal{Q}$ is a commutative W*-algebra on $\mathcal{H}$, then there exists a family $\mathcal{F}$ of mutually orthogonal projections in $\mathcal{Q}$ whose least upper bound is I and such that for any $P \in \mathcal{F}$, the contraction of $\mathcal{Q}$ to $P\mathcal{H}$ is countably decomposable.

Let $\mathcal{F}$ be a family of projections in $\mathcal{Q}$ which is maximal with respect to the properties: 1) the elements of $\mathcal{F}$ are mutually orthogonal, 2) if $P \in \mathcal{F}$, then the contraction of $\mathcal{Q}$ to $P\mathcal{H}$ is countably decomposable. We show that $\bigcup_{P \in \mathcal{F}} P = I$. For otherwise, there exists a nonzero element z in $(I-Q)\mathcal{H}$, where $Q = \bigcup_{P \in \mathcal{F}} P$, and putting R_o for the least upper bound of the projections R in $\mathcal{Q}$ which are bounded by $I-Q$ and such that $Rz = 0$, $I-Q-R_o$ is orthogonal to all the elements of $\mathcal{F}$, is nonzero as $z \neq 0$, and $\mathcal{Q}$ has the relative separating vector z on $(I-Q-R_o)\mathcal{H}$, so that by Lemma 2.5 the contraction of $\mathcal{Q}$ to $(I-Q-R_o)\mathcal{H}$ is countably decomposable.

LEMMA 2.8. Let $\mathcal{Q}$ be a commutative W*-algebra containing I. For each cardinal number $n > 0$ let R_n be the least upper bound of the projections S in $\mathcal{Q}$ such that the contraction of A to $S\mathcal{H}$ has uniform multiplicity n. Then $\bigcup_n R_n = I$.

Set $Q = \bigcup_n R_n$ and as the basis of an indirect proof, assume $Q \neq I$. Let the contraction of $\mathcal{Q}$ to $(I-Q)\mathcal{H}$ be denoted as $\mathcal{Q}_1$, and let P_1 be a nonzero projection in $\mathcal{Q}_1$ such that the contraction $\mathcal{Q}_2$ of $\mathcal{Q}_1$ to $P_1(I-Q)\mathcal{H}$ is countably-decomposable; by Lemma 2.7, P_1 exists, and $P_1(I-Q)\mathcal{H} \neq 0$. If P_1 is the contraction to $(I-Q)\mathcal{H}$ of the projection P in $\mathcal{Q}$ (that such a projection P exists is easily verified), then we can write $P_1(I-Q)\mathcal{H} = P(I-Q)\mathcal{H}$. By Lemma 2.6, there exists a nonzero projection N_2 in $\mathcal{Q}_2$ such that the contraction of $\mathcal{Q}_2$ to

$N_2 P(I-Q)H$ has uniform multiplicity, say n, and obviously $N_2 P(I-Q)H \neq 0$.
Now if N_1 is a projection in Q_1 whose contraction to $P(I-Q)H$ is N_2,
and if N is a projection in Q whose contraction to $(I-Q)H$ is N_1
(the existence of these projections being clear), then the contraction of
Q_2 to $N_2 P(I-Q)H$ is the same as the contraction of Q to $NP(I-Q)H$.
It follows that $NP(I-Q) \leq R_n$ or $NP(I-Q)R_n = NP(I-Q)$, which by the definitions of R_n and Q implies that $NP(I-Q) = 0$, a contradiction.

LEMMA 2.9. <u>Let</u> Q <u>be a</u> <u>commutative W*-algebra</u> <u>of</u> <u>uniform</u> <u>multi-</u>
<u>plicity</u> n <u>and also</u> <u>of</u> <u>uniform multiplicity</u> m. <u>Then</u> $n \aleph_0 = m \aleph_0$.

If P is a nonzero projection in the algebra of operators Q
on H such that the contraction Q_1 of Q to PH is countably decomposable, then by Lemma 2.1, Q_1 is of uniform multiplicities both n and
m. Hence by Lemma 2.7 it suffices to prove the present lemma under the assumption (which we now make) that Q is countably decomposable. Let Q
be unitarily equivalent on the one hand to an n-fold copy of the masa algebra M on K , and on the other to an m-fold copy of the masa algebra N
on L .

Now Q is algebraically isomorphic to both M and N , and
hence both of these algebras are countably decomposable. By Lemma 2.5 there
exist separating vectors u and v for M on K and N on L respectively. Now the closure of Mu is invariant under M so that the
projection P on this closure commutes with each element of M. As M
is maximal abelian, $P \in M$. Obviously $(I-P)u = 0$, and since u is a
separating vector for M , $I-P = 0$, which shows that the closure of Mu
is K , i. e., u is a cyclic vector for M . Similarly v is a cyclic
vector for N on L .

It follows from the definition of uniform multiplicity that H
is the direct sum of n mutually orthogonal subspaces K_μ ($\mu \in S$,

where S is an index set of cardinal number n) each of which is invariant under $\mathcal{Q}$ and such that the contraction of $\mathcal{Q}$ to $\mathcal{K}_\mu$ is unitarily equivalent to $\mathcal{M}$ on $\mathcal{K}$; and $\mathcal{H}$ is also the direct sum of m mutually orthogonal subspaces $\mathcal{L}_\nu$ ($\nu \in$ T, T being an index set of cardinal m), where $\mathcal{Q}$ leaves each of the $\mathcal{L}_\nu$ invariant and whose contraction to any $\mathcal{L}_\nu$ is unitarily equivalent to $\mathcal{N}$ on $\mathcal{L}$. By the preceding paragraph, there exist vectors $x_\mu \in \mathcal{K}_\mu$ and $y_\nu \in \mathcal{L}_\nu$ such that $\mathcal{Q} x_\mu$ is dense in $\mathcal{K}_\mu$ and $\mathcal{Q} y_\nu$ is dense in $\mathcal{L}_\nu$. Now the projection $x_{\mu\nu}$ of x_μ onto $\mathcal{L}_\nu$ vanishes, except for countably many ν , so that the set of all indices ν for which $x_{\mu\nu} \neq 0$ for some μ has cardinal number at most $\aleph_0$ n. But for every ν there is a μ such that $x_{\mu\nu} \neq 0$, for otherwise, taking λ to be an index in T such that $x_{\mu\lambda} = 0$ for all μ , then clearly x_μ is orthogonal to $\mathcal{L}_\lambda$ for all $\mu \in$ S. In particular, $(x_\mu , Ay_\lambda) = 0$ for all $A \in \mathcal{Q}$ and $\mu \in$ S, or $(A*x_\mu , y_\lambda) = 0$ for $A \in \mathcal{Q}$ and $\mu \in$ S. Now the $A*x_\mu$ span $\mathcal{K}_\mu$ as A ranges over $\mathcal{Q}$, and so it follows from the last equation that $(z_\mu , y_\lambda) = 0$ for all z_μ in $\mathcal{K}_\mu$. Since the $\mathcal{K}_\mu$ span $\mathcal{H}$, it results that $(z, y_\lambda) = 0$ for all $z \in \mathcal{H}$, which implies $y_\lambda = 0$, a contradiction. Thus the cardinal number m of T is at most $\aleph_0$ n. By symmetry, $n \leq \aleph_0$ m, and it follows that $n \aleph_0 = m \aleph_0$.

LEMMA 2.10. <u>Let</u> $\mathcal{M}$ <u>be a countably decomposable masa algebra of operators on the Hilbert space</u> $\mathcal{K}$. <u>Let</u> x <u>be a cyclic vector for</u> $\mathcal{M}$ <u>and let</u> $\{y_i\}$ <u>be an arbitrary sequence of vectors in</u> $\mathcal{H}$. <u>Then there exists a nonzero projection</u> P <u>in</u> $\mathcal{M}$ <u>such that</u> $Py_i \in \mathcal{M}$ x (i = 1,2,...).

We note that as shown in the proof of Lemma 2.9, there does actually exist a cyclic vector for $\mathcal{M}$ on $\mathcal{K}$ (in fact, any separating vector is such). By Lemma 1.2, we may assume that $\mathcal{M}$ is the algebra of all multiplications by bounded measurable functions on L_2 over a finite

measure space $M = (R, \mathcal{R}, r)$. It is clear from the fact that $\mathcal{M}x$ is
dense in $L_2(M)$ that $x(a) \neq 0$ a. e. on M. Now setting $E_{ij} =$
$[a \mid \; |y_i(a)| \; < \; j \, |x(a)| \,]$, it follows that $\bigcup_j E_{ij}$ differs from R
by a set of measure zero, and hence there is a j_i such that $r(R - E_{ij_i})$
$< r(R)2^{-i-1}$. Putting $E = \bigcap_i E_{ij_i}$, it results that $r(R - E) \leq$
$\sum_i r(R - E_{ij_i}) < (1/2)r(R)$. Now taking P to be the operation of
multiplication by the characteristic function of E, we have $Py_i \in \mathcal{M}x$,
for Py_i is the product of x and the function, bounded by j_i , which
equals $y_i(a)(x(a))^{-1}$ for $a \in E$ and equals zero elsewhere.

Our proof of the next lemma utilizes a simplification of a device
employed by Nakano [6] in connection with a similar result for the case
of separable Hilbert spaces.

LEMMA 2.11. <u>Suppose a commutative W*-algebra has uniform multi-
plicities both</u> n <u>and</u> m, <u>where</u> n <u>is finite and</u> $m \leq \aleph_0$. <u>Then</u> n = m.

As in the proof of Lemma 2.9, we can confine our attention to the
case in which $\mathcal{Q}$ is countably decomposable and obtain subspaces $\mathcal{K}_\mu$ and
$\mathcal{L}_\nu$ of the space $\mathcal{H}$ on which $\mathcal{Q}$ acts, and vectors x_μ and y_ν in
$\mathcal{K}_\mu$ and $\mathcal{L}_\nu$ such that $\mathcal{Q}x_\mu$ and $\mathcal{Q}y_\nu$ are dense in $\mathcal{K}_\mu$ and $\mathcal{L}_\nu$
respectively, and with $\mathcal{H}$ the direct sum of the $\mathcal{K}_\mu$ and also the direct
sum of the $\mathcal{L}_\nu$ (here $\mu = 1,2,\ldots,n$ and $\nu = 1,2,\ldots,m$ if m is
finite and $\nu = 1,2,\ldots$ otherwise). Putting U_μ for a unitary transformation from $\mathcal{K}$ onto $\mathcal{K}_\mu$ which implements the equivalence of $\mathcal{M}$ and
the contraction of $\mathcal{Q}$ to $\mathcal{K}_\mu$, and x' for a cyclic vector for $\mathcal{M}$, we
can clearly take $x_\mu = U_\mu x'$ without essential loss of generality. Now
putting $y_{\nu\mu}$ for the projection of y_ν onto $\mathcal{K}_\mu$, we evidently have
$y_\nu = \sum_\mu y_{\nu\mu}$. Now setting $y'_{\nu\mu} = U_\mu^{-1}y_{\nu\mu}$ it results from the
preceding lemma that there exists a nonzero projection P' in $\mathcal{M}$ such
that $P'y'_{\nu\mu} \in \mathcal{M}x'$. Now putting P for the projection in $\mathcal{Q}$ which is

24   I. E. Segal

unitarily equivalent via the given transformation to the n-fold copy of P'
(i. e. the contraction of P to $\mathcal{K}_\mu$ is $U_\mu P' U_\mu^{-1}$), then $P \neq 0$. It
is easily seen from the relation $P' y'_{\nu\mu} \in \mathcal{M} x'$ that $P y_{\nu\mu} \in \mathcal{Q} x_\mu$
for all μ and ν, say $P y_{\nu\mu} = T_{\nu\mu} x_\mu$; multiplying this equation
by P shows that we can suppose $T_{\nu\mu} = P T_{\nu\mu}$.

It follows that $P y_\nu = \sum_{\nu=1}^{n} T_{\nu\mu} x_\mu$, for all ν . Now we
assume $m > n$ and derive a contradiction. We use the fact that in an r-
dimensional module over a commutative ring with unit, any $r + 1$ elements
are linearly dependent over the ring (see $[4]$, Th.51). We apply this to
the module over $P\mathcal{Q}$ of all ordered n-tuples of elements of PQ, and in
particular to the $n + 1$ n-tuples $(T_{\nu 1}, T_{\nu 2}, \ldots, T_{\nu n})$ ($\nu = 1, 2, \ldots, n{+}1$).
It results that there exist elements $S_1, S_2, \ldots, S_{n+1}$ of $P\mathcal{Q}$ which are
not all zero and such that $\sum_{\nu=1}^{n+1} T_{\nu\mu} S_\nu = 0$. Hence $\sum_{\nu=1}^{n+1} S_\nu P y_\nu$
$= 0$, or $\sum_{\nu=1}^{n+1} S_\nu y_\nu = 0$. As $S_\nu y_\nu \in \mathcal{L}_\nu$, and since the $\mathcal{L}_\nu$
are mutually orthogonal, we have $S_\nu y_\nu = 0$. The circumstance that y_ν
is a separating vector for $\mathcal{Q}$ now implies that $S_\nu = 0$ ($\nu = 1, \ldots,$
n+1), a contradiction.

      LEMMA 2.12. <u>With the notation of Lemma 2.8, the</u> R_n <u>are mutually</u>
<u>orthogonal.</u>

      For if $R_n R_m \neq 0$, the contraction of $\mathcal{Q}$ to $R_m \mathcal{H}$ is of uni-
form multiplicity m by Lemma 2.4, so that by Lemma 2.1, the contraction
of $\mathcal{Q}$ to $R_n(R_m \mathcal{H})$ likewise has uniform multiplicity m. By symmetry,
the same contraction also has uniform multiplicity n. It follows from
Lemma 2.10, that either $m = n$ or else one of m and n is finite and
the other is not greater than $\aleph_o$. By Lemma 2.11, $m = n$ in the latter
case also.

      PROOF OF THEOREM. With R_n as in Lemma 2.8, we have, putting
R_0 for I-E, where E is the maximal projection in $\mathcal{Q}$, $\bigcup_n R_n = I$ by

Lemma 2.8, and the contraction of $\mathcal{Q}$ to $R_n \mathcal{H}$ has uniform multiplicity n by Lemma 2.4. Now if P_n is for each cardinal n a projection in $\mathcal{Q}$ with the properties stated in the theorem, then from the definition of R_n, it is clear that $P_n \leq R_n$. Now $\bigcup_n P_n = I$, but the R_n are mutually disjoint by the preceding lemma, so that $P_m \cap R_n = 0$ for $m \neq n$, and it results that $R_n = P_n$.

5. <u>Unitary invariants of commutative W*-algebras and of SA operators</u>. In this section we first prove a theorem which gives a simple complete set of unitary invariants for a commutative W*-algebra. Assuming, in order to avoid a trivial complication, that the identity is in the algebra, these invariants consist of Boolean rings $B(n)$, one such ring being attached to each cardinal number (or multiplicity) n, and vanishing for sufficiently large n. These rings are (lattice-theoretically) complete measure rings, and all such rings may occur. The classification theorem of Maharam [3] for measure rings is stated for the σ-finite case, but there is no difficulty in extending it to an arbitrary complete measure ring. The use of this extended classification provides a still simpler set of invariants, consisting essentially of a function on pairs of cardinals to the cardinals, - if f is this function, $f(m, n)$ is the number of direct summands of the measure ring of the infinite product measure space I^m, where I is the unit interval under Lebesgue measure, which occur in (the direct decomposition into homogeneous parts of) $B(n)$, but the discrete part of $B(n)$ and the case $1 \leq m \leq \aleph_o$ must be treated separately. The validity of these invariants, whose range is clear, follows at once from the following theorem together with Maharam's theorem, and we refer to [3], from which the mode of derivation of these cardinals is clear. Thus the most general commutative W*-algebra can be regarded as completely and rather explicitly known.

    <u>Definition 5.1</u>. Let $\mathcal{A}$ be a commutative W*-algebra, and let $\{P_n\}$ be as in Theorem 2. The Boolean ring $B(n)$ of all projections in the contraction of $\mathcal{A}$ to the range of P_n (which ring is shown below to be a complete measure-bearing ring) is called the <u>measure ring of</u> $\mathcal{A}$ <u>for the multiplicity</u> n.

    THEOREM 3. <u>Two commutative W*-algebras are unitarily equivalent if and only if their measure rings for the same multiplicities are algebraically isomorphic, and also the maximal (necessarily closed) linear manifolds which they annihilate have the same dimensions.</u>

    For any commutative W*-algebra $\mathcal{A}$, the contraction of $\mathcal{A}$ to $P_n\mathcal{H}$, where $\mathcal{H}$ is the space on which $\mathcal{A}$ acts and P_n is as in Theorem 2, will be called the <u>part of</u> $\mathcal{A}$ <u>of uniform multiplicity</u> <u>n</u>. Now if C and $\mathcal{D}$ are unitarily equivalent W*-algebras it is clear from Theorem 2 that their parts C_n and $\mathcal{D}_n$ of uniform multiplicity n are unitarily equivalent, and hence their measure rings for the same multiplicity are algebraically isomorphic. It is obvious that the dimensions of the maximal closed linear manifolds which C and $\mathcal{D}$ annihilate are equal.

    Now suppose that C and $\mathcal{D}$ are commutative W*-algebras whose measure rings for the same multiplicities are algebraically isomorphic, and such that the maximal linear manifolds which they annihilate have the same dimension. We shall show that C and $\mathcal{D}$ are unitarily equivalent, and for this purpose we may evidently assume that both C and $\mathcal{D}$ contain the identity operators on the respective spaces on which they act. Let C_n and $\mathcal{D}_n$ be the parts of C and $\mathcal{D}$ of uniform multiplicity n, and let $\mathcal{M}_n$ and $\mathcal{N}_n$ be masa algebras, to n-fold copies of which C_n and $\mathcal{D}_n$ are respectively unitarily equivalent. Then it is clear from the definition of n-fold copy that C_n and $\mathcal{M}_n$ on the one hand and $\mathcal{D}_n$ and $\mathcal{N}_n$ on the other, are algebraically isomorphic. Now $\mathcal{M}_n$ and $\mathcal{N}_n$ are unique within unitary equivalence, for taking the case of $\mathcal{M}_n$, if $\mathcal{C}_n$ is also unitarily equivalent to an n-fold copy of the masa algebra $\mathcal{L}_n$, then $\mathcal{C}_n$ and $\mathcal{L}_n$ are algebraically isomorphic and so $\mathcal{M}_n$ and $\mathcal{L}_n$ are algebraically isomorphic. Now $\mathcal{M}_n$ and $\mathcal{N}_n$ are both multiplication algebras of localizable spaces, within unitary equivalence, by Theorem 1, and it is shown in $\begin{bmatrix}10\end{bmatrix}$ that if two such algebras are algebraically isomorphic, then they are unitarily equivalent.

Let $\mathcal{M}_n$ and $\mathcal{N}_n$ be respectively (unitarily equivalent to) the multiplication algebras of the localizable measure spaces M_n and N_n. The Boolean ring of projections in $\mathcal{C}_n$ is plainly algebraically isomorphic with the ring of projections in $\mathcal{M}_n$ which in turn is readily seen to be isomorphic with the measure ring of M_n. Similarly the Boolean ring of projections in $\mathcal{D}_n$ is algebraically isomorphic to the measure ring of N_n. Hence $\mathcal{M}_n$ and $\mathcal{N}_n$ have algebraically isomorphic measure rings. By a result in $\begin{bmatrix}10\end{bmatrix}$ their multiplication algebras are then unitarily equivalent. Thus $\mathcal{M}_n$ and $\mathcal{N}_n$ are unitarily equivalent, and it follows that $\mathcal{C}_n$ and $\mathcal{D}_n$ are unitarily equivalent. It is straightforward to show from this that $\mathcal{C}$ and $\mathcal{D}$ are unitarily equivalent.

Next we obtain a complete set of unitary invariants for a SA operator, this set being due to Wecken $\begin{bmatrix}14\end{bmatrix}$ and to Plessner and Rokhlin $\begin{bmatrix}8\end{bmatrix}$, some of whose techniques we use. Before stating the basic theorem we use the foregoing theory to reduce the problem to the situation treated in the theorem. If T is a SA operator, and if T_n is its part of uniform multiplicity n (= contraction of T to the range of P_n, where P_n is as in Theorem 2, $\mathcal{A}$ being the W*-algebra generated by T), then T_n is unitarily equivalent to an n-fold copy of an operator S_n with simple spectrum (i. e. the W*-algebra generated by S_n is masa). By Theorem 1, S_n can be taken to be the operation of multiplication by some function, on $L_2(M_n)$, for some localizable measure space M_n. It is easily seen that a

complete set of unitary invariants for the S_n is also a complete set for
T, and so the problem is reduced to the essentially measure-theoretic one
of determining when two multiplication operators, each of which has simple
spectrum, are unitarily equivalent. The classification of Maharam could be
used to reduce the problem further to the case when the measure spaces in
question are homogeneous. Naturally it is a restriction on a measure space
for it to admit a multiplication operator with simple spectrum, but we
shall not discuss the nature of this restriction, which at present is unclear (except for the fact, which follows from Corollary 5.3 without difficulty, that the separability character of the space must not exceed the
cardinality of the continuum).

Thus in order to obtain a complete set of unitary invariants for
a SA operator, it is sufficient, in view of the foregoing, to obtain such a
set for SA operators with simple spectrum, and in the remainder of this
section we consider only such operators. We note that if attention is
restricted to SA operators with simple spectra which are unitarily equivalent to multiplication operators on finite measure spaces (and for operators on separable Hilbert spaces this is always the case, as it means that
the W*-algebra generated by the operator is countably decomposable), the
operator is determined within unitary equivalence by its spectrum together
with its spectral null sets, - for separable Hilbert spaces this was proved
by Nakano [6] . The invariants given by the following theorem for the
general case are a kind of generalization of these invariants. Another set
of invariants for the general case, more closely related to those for the
case of finite measure spaces, but in some respects more complicated than
the present ones is due to Nakano [7] .

Definition 5.2. For an arbitrary SA operator T on a Hilbert
space $\mathcal{H}$, the weighted spectrum $\mathcal{E}(T)$ is the family of all (finite regular) measures m on the reals of the form $m(B) = (E(B)x, x)$, where B

is an arbitrary Borel subset of the reals, $E(.)$ is the spectral measure associated with T and x is arbitrary in $\mathcal{H}$. (It is easily seen that m is concentrated on the spectrum of T, as this term is usually defined).

THEOREM 4. (Wecken-Plessner-Rokhlin). **Two SA operators on Hilbert spaces with simple spectra are unitarily equivalent if and only if their weighted spectra are the same.**

It is clear that if two SA operators are unitarily equivalent, then their weighted spectra are the same. Now let T and T' be SA operators with simple spectra on Hilbert spaces $\mathcal{H}$ and $\mathcal{H}'$ respectively whose weighted spectra $\mathcal{E}$ and $\mathcal{E}'$ are the same. To show that T and T' are unitarily equivalent we require two lemmas, which are essentially contained in the work of the authors mentioned. In connection with these lemmas we recall that two measures (on the same ring of sets) are said to be orthogonal if the only measure absolutely continuous with respect to both of them is the zero measure.

LEMMA 4.1. **Let** x **and** y **be elements of** $\mathcal{H}$, **let** $\mathcal{A}$ **be the W*-algebra generated by** T, **and let** $E(.)$ **be the spectral measure associated with** T. **Then** $\mathcal{A}x$ **is orthogonal to** $\mathcal{A}y$ **if and only if** m_x **is orthogonal to** m_y, **where for any** $z \in \mathcal{H}$, m_z **is the measure on the Borel subsets of the reals given by the equation** $m_z(B) = (E(B)z, z)$.

We observe to begin with that if z is in the closure $\mathcal{K}_x$ of $\mathcal{A}x$, then m_z is absolutely continuous with respect to m_x. For if $\{V_n\}$ is a sequence in $\mathcal{A}$ such that $V_n x \longrightarrow z$, then $m_z(B) = \|E(B)x\|^2 = \lim_n \|E(B)V_n x\|^2 = \lim_n \|V_n E(B)x\|^2$, and if $m_x(B) = 0$ we have $E(B)x = 0$ and it results that $m_z(B) = 0$. We note also that the projection P_x of $\mathcal{H}$ onto $\mathcal{K}_x$ is in $\mathcal{A}$, for as $\mathcal{K}_x$ is invariant under $\mathcal{A}$, $P_x \in \mathcal{A}'$, but $\mathcal{A}' = \mathcal{A}$. Similarly the projection P_y of

$\mathcal{H}$ onto the closure $\mathcal{K}_y$ of $\mathcal{Q}_y$ is in $\mathcal{Q}$. Thus P_x and P_y commute.

Now suppose that m_x is orthogonal to m_y. By the last observation, to show that $\mathcal{K}_x$ and $\mathcal{K}_y$ are orthogonal it suffices to show that their intersection is 0. Now if $z \in \mathcal{K}_x \cap \mathcal{K}_y$, then as shown in the preceding paragraph m_z is orthogonal to both m_x and m_y, so $m_z = 0$, from which it follows trivially that $z = 0$.

Next we assume that $\mathcal{Q}_x$ is orthogonal to $\mathcal{Q}_y$ and show that then m_x and m_y are orthogonal. As the basis of an indirect proof, let n be a nonzero finite regular measure on the reals which is absolutely continuous with respect to both m_x and m_y. By the Radon-Nikodym theorem, there exist m_x and m_y integrable non-negative functions h_x and h_y respectively such that $n(B) = \int_B h_x(\lambda)dm_x(\lambda) = \int_B h_y(\lambda)dm_y(\lambda)$, where B is an arbitrary Borel set. Putting $g_x(\lambda) = \min \{1, h_x(\lambda)\}$ and $g_y(\lambda) = \min \{1, h_y(\lambda)\}$, and setting n_x and n_y for the set functions defined by the equations $n_x(B) = \int_B g_x(\lambda)dm_x(\lambda)$ and $n_y(B) = \int_B g_y(\lambda)dm_y(\lambda)$, then it is clear that n and n_x are absolutely continuous with respect to each other, that the same is true of n and n_y, and that for any Borel set B we have both $n_x(B) \leq m_x(B)$ and $n_y(B) \leq m_y(B)$. In particular, n_x and n_y are absolutely continuous with respect to each other and so by the Radon-Nikodym theorem we have $n_y(B) = \int_B f(\lambda)dn_x(\lambda)$, for some n_x-integrable function f. Defining m on Borel sets B by the equation $m(B) = \int_B f'(\lambda)dn_x(\lambda)$, where $f'(\lambda) = \min \{1, f(\lambda)\}$, it is evident that $m(B) \leq n_y(B)$, $m(B) \leq m_x(B)$, and $m \neq 0$. Thus m is a nonzero regular measure on the reals such that $m(B) \leq m_x(B)$ and $m(B) \leq m_y(B)$ for all B.

Applying the Radon-Nikodym theorem once more, we have $m(B) = \int_B f_x(\lambda)dm_x(\lambda) = \int_B f_y(\lambda)dm_y(\lambda)$, where f_x and f_y are m_x and m_y integrable functions respectively, which are bounded by unity. As m_x and m_y are regular measures, f_x and f_y can be taken to be Baire functions. Now $f_x(T)$ is a positive semidefinite SA operator and so has the form V^2 for some SA operator V in $\mathcal{A}$. Clearly $m(B) =$

$$\int_B f_x(\lambda)d(E_\lambda x, x) \;=\; (f_x(T)E(B)x, x) \;=\; (V^2 E(B)x, x) \;=\; (E(B)Vx, Vx)$$

$= m_{x'}(B)$ where $x' = Vx$. Similarly $m = m_{y'}$ for some $y' \in \mathcal{A}y$. Thus $(E(B)x', x') = (E(B)y', y')$ for all Borel sets B. As the $E(E)$ generate $\mathcal{A}$ in the strong operator topology, it follows that $(Sx', x') = (Sy', y')$ for all operators S in $\mathcal{A}$. Taking S to be first the projection on $\mathcal{H}_x$ and next to be the projection on $\mathcal{K}_y$ shows that $x' = y' = 0$, so $m = 0$, a contradiction.

LEMMA 4.2. <u>Let</u> x <u>be an arbitrary nonzero element of</u> $\mathcal{H}$. <u>The contraction of</u> T <u>to the closure of</u> $\mathcal{A}x$ <u>is unitarily equivalent to the operation of multiplication by the coordinate function</u> λ <u>on</u> $L_2(\mathbb{M}_x)$, <u>where</u> $\mathbb{M}_x$ <u>is the regular measure space on the reals</u>, $-\infty < \lambda < \infty$, <u>with measure</u> m_x.

A proof of this can be given which is a straightforward adaptation and simplification of the proof of Lemma 1.2 and we omit further details.

<u>Completion of proof of theorem</u>. Let $\mathcal{F}$ be a subset of the weighted spectrum $\mathcal{E}(T)$ of T which is maximal with respect to its elements being mutually orthogonal and nonzero; the existence of $\mathcal{F}$ is clear from transfinite induction. For each $\rho \in \mathcal{F}$, let x $(= x(\rho))$ and x' $(= x'(\rho))$ be elements of $\mathcal{H}$ and $\mathcal{H}'$ respectively such that $\rho(B) = (E(B)x, x) = (E'(B)x', x')$, where $E'(.)$ is the spectral measure associated with T'. We show now that the $\mathcal{A}x_\rho$ span $\mathcal{H}$, $\rho \in \mathcal{F}$. Let $\mathcal{N}$ be the closed linear manifold spanned by the $\mathcal{A}x_\rho$, $\rho \in \mathcal{F}$, and let $\mathcal{S}$ be its orthogonal complement in $\mathcal{H}$. Clearly $\mathcal{N}$ is invariant under $\mathcal{A}$, and if z is any nonzero element of S, $m_z \in \mathcal{E}(T)$ and m_z is orthogonal to all the m_{x_ρ} with $\rho \in \mathcal{F}$, by Lemma 4.1. Hence $\mathcal{S} = 0$.

I. E. Segal

Thus $\mathcal{H}$ is the direct sum of the $\mathcal{H}_\rho$ ($\rho \in \mathcal{F}$), where $\mathcal{H}_\rho$ is the closure of $\mathcal{Q}x_\rho$, and by symmetry $\mathcal{H}'$ is the direct sum of the $\mathcal{H}'_\rho$ ($\rho \in \mathcal{F}$), where $\mathcal{H}'_\rho$ is the closure of $\mathcal{Q}_1 x'_\rho$, $\mathcal{Q}_1$ being the W*-algebra generated by T'. By Lemma 4.2, the contraction of T to $\mathcal{H}_\rho$ is unitarily equivalent to the operation of multiplication by the coordinate function on $L_2(M_{x_\rho})$ and hence equivalent to the contraction of T' to $\mathcal{H}'_\rho$. It follows without difficulty that T and T' are unitarily equivalent.

6. <u>Applications</u>. In this section we make a number of applications of the preceding structure theory, mainly to spectral theory. Our basic result is as follows.

THEOREM 5. <u>If</u> $\mathcal{Q}$ <u>is a commutative W*-algebra there is a maximal abelian W*-algebra</u> $\mathcal{M}$ <u>to which</u> $\mathcal{Q}$ <u>is algebraically isomorphic (with preservation of adjoints). Any such isomorphism</u> φ <u>of</u> $\mathcal{Q}$ <u>onto</u> $\mathcal{M}$ <u>is bicontinuous in the weak topology and has the property that if</u> f <u>is any bounded Baire function on the complex numbers, then for any operator</u> T <u>in</u> $\mathcal{Q}$, $\varphi(f(T)) = f(\varphi(T))$. <u>The algebra</u> $\mathcal{M}$ <u>is unique within unitary equivalence, and the dimension of the space on which it acts is not greater than the corresponding dimension for</u> $\mathcal{Q}$.

If φ_1 and φ_2 are algebraic isomorphisms of the W*-algebra $\mathcal{Q}$ onto a masa algebra $\mathcal{M}$, then $\psi = \varphi_1 \varphi_2^{-1}$ is an algebraic isomorphism of $\mathcal{M}$ onto itself. As an algebraic isomorphism between masa algebras is induced by some unitary transformation between the corresponding Hilbert spaces [10], there is a unitary operator U on the Hilbert space $\mathcal{H}$ on which $\mathcal{M}$ acts, such that $\psi(T) = U*TU$, $T \in \mathcal{M}$. Hence to show that any isomorphism of $\mathcal{Q}$ onto $\mathcal{M}$ is bicontinuous in the weak topology, and preserves the operational calculus, it suffices to show that any one isomorphism has these properties. Moreover, if $\mathcal{A}$ is algebraically iso-morphic to a masa algebra $\mathcal{N}$, by the result just quoted $\mathcal{M}$ and $\mathcal{N}$ are unitarily equivalent, i. e., $\mathcal{M}$ is essentially unique. Hence to conclude the proof of the theorem it suffices to show that for the given W*-algebra $\mathcal{A}$, there exists an isomorphism of $\mathcal{A}$ onto a masa algebra $\mathcal{M}$ which is weakly bicontinuous and preserves the operational calculus.

Let P_n be as in Theorem 2, and let the contraction of $\mathcal{A}$ to $P_n \mathcal{H}$ $(n > 0)$ be unitarily equivalent to an n-fold copy of the masa alge-bra $\mathcal{M}_n$ on $\mathcal{K}_n$. By Theorem 1 we may assume that $\mathcal{K}_n$ consists of L_2 over a localizable measure space $M_n = (R_n, \mathcal{R}_n, r_n)$ and that $\mathcal{M}_n$ is the multiplication algebra of M_n. Let the measure space $M = (R, \mathcal{R}, r)$ be the direct sum of the M_n, for all n, so that $L_2(M)$ can be identified in a clear fashion with the direct sum $\mathcal{K}$ of the $\mathcal{K}_n$, and let $\mathcal{M}$ be the algebra on $\mathcal{K}$ corresponding to the multiplication algebra of M. Then $\mathcal{M}$ is readily seen to consist of all operators T whose contraction T_n to $\mathcal{K}_n$ is in $\mathcal{M}_n$ and such that $\|T_n\|$ is bounded. Now $\mathcal{M}$ is masa, for if $T \in \mathcal{M}'$, and if Q_n is the projection of $\mathcal{K}$ onto $\mathcal{K}_n$, then as plainly $Q_n \in \mathcal{M}$, $TQ_n = Q_n T$ so that T leaves $\mathcal{K}_n$ invariant. Putting T_n for the contraction of T to $\mathcal{K}_n$, then $(UV)_n = U_n V_n$ for any operators U and V leaving $\mathcal{K}_n$ invariant, and it follows that $T_n S_n = S_n T_n$ for $S \in \mathcal{M}$. Hence $T_n \in \mathcal{M}_n'$, and as obviously $\|T_n\| \leq \|T\|$, we have $T \in \mathcal{M}$. (The masa character of $\mathcal{M}$ also follows directly from a result in $[10]$).

Next we define an isomorphism φ of $\mathcal{A}$ onto $\mathcal{M}$. For any operator T in $\mathcal{A}$, let T_n denote its contraction to $P_n \mathcal{H}$, and for any operator U in the contraction of $\mathcal{A}$ to $P_n \mathcal{H}$, let $\psi_n(U)$ be the oper-ator in $\mathcal{M}_n$ whose n-fold copy U is taken into by the unitary equivalence of $\mathcal{A}$ with the n-fold copy of $\mathcal{M}_n$. It is easily seen that $\|\psi_n(U)\|$ $= \|U\|$, so that there exists a (clearly unique) operator $\varphi(T)$ on $\mathcal{K}$

whose contraction to $\mathcal{K}_n$ is $\psi_n(T_n)$, and evidently $\varphi(T) \in \mathcal{M}$. Now ψ_n is an isomorphism, and it follows without difficulty that so also is φ.

To see that φ is weakly continuous it is sufficient, by virtue of the linearity of φ, to show that it is weakly continuous at 0. Now $[T \in \mathcal{Q} \mid \quad |(Tx_i, y_i)| < \varepsilon , i \in F]$, where $\varepsilon > 0$, F is finite, and the x_i and y_i are elements of $\mathcal{H}$, is an arbitrary neighborhood of 0 in $\mathcal{Q}$ in the weak topology. A general neighborhood of 0 in $\mathcal{M}$ in the weak topology is $[T' \in \mathcal{M} \mid (T'x_i', y_i')| < \varepsilon , i \in F]$, where ε and F are as before and the x_i' and y_i' are in $\mathcal{K}$. For any x in $\mathcal{K}_n$ we define $\rho_n(x)$ to be the element of $P_n \mathcal{H}$ obtained as follows: let $P_n \mathcal{H}$ be the direct sum of the n closed linear subspaces $\mathcal{H}_{nj}$ ($j \in S_n$, where S_n is an index set of cardinal n), where $\mathcal{Q}$ leaves $\mathcal{H}_{nj}$ invariant and has a contraction on $\mathcal{H}_{nj}$ unitarily equivalent, via the unitary operator U_{nj} on $\mathcal{K}_n$ to $\mathcal{H}_{nj}$, to $\mathcal{M}_n$ on $\mathcal{K}_n$ (these subspaces exist because the contraction of $\mathcal{Q}$ to $P_n \mathcal{H}$ has uniform multiplicity n). Let j_n be any element of S_n, and set $\rho_n(x') = U_{nj_n} x'$, $x' \in \mathcal{K}_n$. Now for any element $x \in \mathcal{K}$ we put $\rho(x) = \sum_n \rho_n(x_n)$, where x_n is the projection of x onto $\mathcal{K}_n$. It is easily seen that for any x' and y' in $\mathcal{K}_n$ and $T' \in \mathcal{M}_n$, $(T'x', y') = (\varphi^{-1}(T') \rho_n(x'), \rho_n(y'))$, and it follows that for any x' and y' in $\mathcal{K}$ and T' in $\mathcal{M}$, $(T_n'x_n', y_n')$ $= (\varphi^{-1}(T') \rho_n(x_n'), \rho_n(y_n'))$, where x_n' and y_n' and the projections of x' and y' on $\mathcal{K}_n$ and T_n' is the contraction of T' to $\mathcal{K}_n$. Summing both sides of the last equation over n shows that $(T'x', y') = (\varphi^{-1}(T') \rho(x'), \rho(y'))$. Hence the inverse image under φ of $[T' \in \mathcal{M} \mid \quad |(T'x', y')| < \varepsilon , i \in F]$ is $[T \in \mathcal{Q} \mid \quad |(T \rho(x_i'), \rho(y_i'))| < \varepsilon , i \in F]$, and so is a neighborhood of 0 in $\mathcal{Q}$.

Next we show that φ^{-1} is weakly continuous. It is not difficult to see from the definition of uniform multiplicity that the contraction of $\mathcal{a}$ to $P_n \mathcal{H}$ is unitarily equivalent, say via the unitary transformation V_n on $P_n \mathcal{H}$, to the algebra of all multiplications by bounded measurable functions on M_n, on $L_2(M_n \times W_n)$, where W_n is the measure space whose set is S_n and in which each finite subset is measurable and has measure equal to its cardinal. Now if x and y are arbitrary in $P_n \mathcal{H}$, say $V_n x = x(p, i)$ and $V_n y = y(p, i)$ $(p \in R_n, i \in S_n)$ and T is arbitrary in $\mathcal{a}$, then $V_n T_n V_n^{-1}$ is the operation of multiplication by a bounded measurable function $t_n(p)$, where T_n is the contraction of T to $P_n \mathcal{H}$, and $(Tx, y) = \int_{M_n \times W_n} t_n(p)x(p, i)y(p, i)dr(p)di$, and integrating first with respect to i, this equals $\int_{M_n} t_n(p)w(p)dr(p)$, where $w(p) = \sum_{i \in S_n} x(p, i)y(p, i)$, so $w \in L_1(M_n)$. Writing w in the form $w(p) = x'(p)y'(p)$, with x' and y' in $L_2(M_n)$ and with $\|x'\|^2 = \|y'\|^2 = \|w\|_1$, it results that $(Tx, y) = (T'x', y')$, where $T' = \varphi^{-1}(T)$. Now for arbitrary x and y in $\mathcal{H}$ we write $x = \sum_n x_n$ and $y = \sum_n y_n$, with x_n and y_n in $P_n \mathcal{H}$, and summing both sides of the equation $(Tx_n, y_n) = (T'x_n', y_n')$ over n, then $(Tx, y) = (T'x', y')$, where $x' = \sum_n x_n'$ and $y' = \sum_n y_n'$, these sums existing in the sense of unconditional convergence because $\sum_n \|x_n'\|^2 = \sum_n \|w\|_1 = \sum_n \int_{M_n} |\sum_i x_n(p, i)y_n(p, i)| \, dr(p) \le \sum_n \int_{M_n} (\sum_i |x_n(p, i)y_n(p, i)| \, dr(p) = \sum_n \int_{M_n \times W_n} |x_n(p, i)y_n(p, i)| \, dr(p)di \le \sum_n \|x_n\| \|y_n\| \le (\sum_n \|x_n\|^2)(\sum_n \|y_n\|^2) = \|x\| \|y\|$, which is finite; and similarly when x is replaced by y. Hence the image under φ of the neighborhood $[T \in \mathcal{a} | \; |(Tx_i, y_i)| < \varepsilon, \; i \in F]$ of 0 in $\mathcal{a}$ is of the form $[T' \in \mathcal{M} | \; |(T'x_i', y_i')| < \varepsilon]$, with the x_i' and the y_i' in $\mathcal{K}$, and so is a neighborhood of 0 in $\mathcal{M}$. Thus φ^{-1} is weakly continuous.

It remains only to show that $\varphi(f(T)) = f(\varphi(T))$ for any bounded Baire function f, and this we show is valid for any weakly continuous algebraic homomorphism φ. The foregoing equation is obviously valid when f is a polynomial, and it follows from the Weierstrass approximation

theorem that it is then valid for any continuous function f (in view of
the boundedness of the spectra of T and φ(T)). Now let $\mathcal{F}$ be the
collection of all bounded Baire functions for which that equation is valid
(for all T $\in \mathcal{A}$): we show that $\mathcal{F}$ is closed under bounded pointwise
convergence of sequences. Let $\{f_n\}$ be a sequence in $\mathcal{F}$ such that
$f_n(\alpha) \longrightarrow f(\alpha)$ for all complex α , and with $|f_n(.)|$ bounded (n =
1,2,...). It follows from the spectral theorem for normal operators to-
gether with the Lebesgue convergence theorem that the sequence $\{f_n(T)\}$
converges weakly to f(T), and similarly $\{f_n(\varphi(T))\}$ converges weakly
to f(φ(T)). As φ is weakly continuous it results that φ(f(T)) =
f(φ(T)), and hence $\mathcal{F}$ contains all bounded Baire functions, for it is
clear that all such functions are in the smallest collection of functions
containing all bounded continuous functions and closed under bounded point-
wise convergence.

The following result is due originally to von Neumann [13] .

COROLLARY 5.1. <u>For</u> <u>any</u> <u>commutative</u> <u>W∗-algebra</u> $\mathcal{A}$ <u>on a</u> <u>separable</u>
<u>Hilbert</u> <u>space</u> <u>there</u> <u>is a</u> <u>self-adjoint</u> <u>element of</u> $\mathcal{A}$ <u>such</u> <u>that</u> <u>every</u> <u>ele-</u>
<u>ment of</u> $\mathcal{A}$ <u>is a</u> <u>Baire</u> <u>function</u> <u>of</u> T.

Let $\mathcal{M}$ be a masa algebra on $\mathcal{K}$ to which $\mathcal{A}$ is algebraically
isomorphic. By Theorem 1, $\mathcal{M}$ is unitarily equivalent to the multiplication
algebra of some localizable measure space M, and by the preceding theorem
L_2(M), which can be identified with $\mathcal{K}$, is separable. By the known classification of separable measure spaces, M can be taken to be (i. e. has its
measure ring isomorphic to that of) the direct sum of a (possibly vacuous)
real bounded interval under Lebesgue measure and a (possibly vacuous) discrete measure space containing at most a countable number of points, which
can be assumed to lie in some real bounded interval disjoint from the previ-
ous one, and to have finite total measure. The resulting measure space is

finite and regular, and for every measurable function on such a space there is a Baire function equal a. e. to it. It follows that every multiplication on $L_2(M)$ by a bounded measurable function is a bounded Baire function of the operation of multiplying by the coordinate function x. Thus $\mathcal{M}$ consists of the bounded Baire functions of a single SA operator, and by Theorem 4, $\mathcal{a}$ also is such.

The next result was pointed out to us by I. M. Singer.

COROLLARY 5.2. <u>An</u> <u>algebraic</u> <u>isomorphism</u> between <u>two</u> <u>commutative</u> <u>W*-algebras</u> (<u>not</u> <u>necessarily</u> <u>on</u> <u>the</u> <u>same space</u>) <u>is</u> <u>necessarily</u> <u>bicontinuous</u> <u>in</u> <u>the</u> <u>weak</u> <u>topology</u> <u>and</u> <u>preserves</u> <u>the</u> <u>operational</u> <u>calculus</u> <u>for</u> <u>bounded</u> <u>Baire</u> <u>functions</u>.

If ψ is an algebraic isomorphism of the W*-algebra $\mathcal{a}_1$ onto the W*-algebra $\mathcal{a}_2$, and if $\mathcal{M}_1$ and $\mathcal{M}_2$ are masa algebras algebraically isomorphic to $\mathcal{a}_1$ and $\mathcal{a}_2$ respectively, then clearly $\mathcal{M}_1$ and $\mathcal{M}_2$ are algebraically isomorphic. This implies (loc. cit.) that $\mathcal{M}_1$ and $\mathcal{M}_2$ are unitarily equivalent. The corollary now follows from Theorem 4.

In the case of a separable Hilbert space, the W*-algebra generated by a SA operator consists of all bounded Baire functions of the operator. This is no longer the case for Hilbert spaces of higher dimension. The next corollary shows however that with an appropriate generalization of the operational calculus, the result remains valid. We first make the following

<u>Definitions 6.1</u>. A projection P on a Hilbert space is called <u>countably-decomposable</u> relative to a W*-algebra $\mathcal{a}$ if every family of mutually orthogonal projections in $\mathcal{a}$ each of which is bounded by P is at most countable. An operator U on a Hilbert space $\mathcal{H}$ is called an <u>extended</u> <u>Baire</u> <u>function</u> of a normal operator T on $\mathcal{H}$ if for every countably-decomposable projection P in the W*-algebra generated by T

and I, U leaves $P\mathcal{H}$ invariant, and the contraction of U to $P\mathcal{H}$ is (in the usual sense) a bounded Baire function of the contraction of T to $P\mathcal{H}$.

We mention that a very explicit development of an apparently closely related notion of extended function is due to Plessner and Rokhlin [8], who deal with an operational calculus for functions on the reals which depend also on a variable ranging over a certain Boolean algebra.

COROLLARY 5.3. <u>The W∗-algebra generated by a SA operator</u> T <u>and the identity consists of all (bounded) extended Baire functions of</u> T.

Let $\mathcal{A}$ be the W∗-algebra generated by the SA operator T on $\mathcal{H}$ and I, and let S be any extended Baire function of T. To show that S $\in \mathcal{A}$ is equivalent, by a well-known theorem of von Neumann, to showing that S $\in \mathcal{A}''$, or that SU $=$ US for all U $\in \mathcal{A}'$. Now let P be a countably-decomposable projection relative to $\mathcal{A}$ which is in $\mathcal{A}$. Denoting contractions to $P\mathcal{H}$ by subscribing "P", it is clear that S_P is a Baire function of T_P, and that $\mathcal{A}_P$ is generated by T_P and I_P, so $S_P \in (\mathcal{A}_P)''$. Now TU $=$ UT and contracting to $P\mathcal{H}$ yields the equation $(TU)_P = (UT)_P$. As U leaves $P\mathcal{H}$ invariant, it follows that $T_P U_P =$ $U_P T_P$, or $U_P \in (\mathcal{A}_P)'$. It results that $S_P U_P = U_P S_P$, or $(SU)_P = (US)_P$, which by virtue of Lemma 2.7 shows that SU $=$ US.

Now let S be arbitrary in the algebra $\mathcal{A}$ defined above. If P is a countably-decomposable projection in $\mathcal{A}$, then clearly $S_P \in \mathcal{A}_P$ and $\mathcal{A}_P$ is the W∗-algebra generated by T_P and I_P, so it is sufficient for the remainder of the proof to restrict attention to the case in which I is countably decomposable relative to $\mathcal{A}$. By Theorem 4, it may also be assumed that $\mathcal{A}$ is masa. Hence by Theorem 1, Remark 3.1, and Lemmas 1.2 and 2.5, the proof of the corollary will be concluded by establishing the following result.

LEMMA 5.3.1. _Let_ $M = (R, \mathcal{R}, r)$ _be a finite perfect measure space, and let_ k _be a real-valued continuous function on_ M _such that the W$*$-algebra generated by the identity and the operation on_ $L_2(M)$ _of multiplication by_ k, _is the multiplication algebra of_ M. _Then for every real-valued continuous function_ h _on_ M _there is a bounded Baire function_ ρ _such that_ $h(p) = \rho(k(p))$ _almost everywhere on_ M.

Let $\mathcal{S}$ be the σ-ring of all elements of $\mathcal{R}$ of the form $k^{-1}(B)$, where B is a Borel subset of the reals. We show first that every element of $\mathcal{R}$ differs by a null set from some element of $\mathcal{S}$. Let $\mathcal{K}$ be the set of all elements of $\mathcal{H} = L_2(M)$ which are measurable relative to $\mathcal{S}$. By the Riesz-Fischer theorem, $\mathcal{K}$ is a closed linear manifold in $\mathcal{H}$, and it is easily seen to be invariant under the operation T of multiplication by k. Hence K is invariant under the multiplication algebra of $\mathcal{M}$. It can be shown (cf. [12]) that any such manifold consists of all elements of $\mathcal{H}$ which vanish a. e. on some set K in $\mathcal{R}$. But, denoting the characteristic function of any set E as χ_E, we have χ_{R-K} then in $\mathcal{K}$, and as the function 1 which is identically one on R is in $\mathcal{K}$, $1 - \chi_{R-K}$ or χ_K is also in $\mathcal{K}$. This implies that χ_K vanishes a. e. on K, or that K is a null set.

It is clear that adding a constant to k does not materially affect the situation, and hence we may assume that $k(p) \geq 1$ for $p \in R$. Now let h be an arbitrary real-valued bounded measurable function on M, and let τ and ω be the functions on the Borel subsets B of the reals defined as follows: $\tau(B) = \int_E h(p)dr(p)$ and $\omega(B) = \int_E k(p)dr(p)$, where $E = k^{-1}(B)$. It is easily seen that τ and ω are finite regular measures on the reals. We observe now that τ is absolutely continuous with respect to ω, and in fact $|\tau(B)| \leq \|h\|_\infty \int_E dr(p) \leq \|h\|_\infty \int_E k(p)dr(p) = \|h\|_\infty \omega(B)$. Hence there exists a bounded

ω -measurable real-valued function ψ on the reals such that $\tau(B) = \int_B \psi(x)d\,\omega(x)$. In a finite regular measure space, any bounded measurable function is equal a. e. to some bounded Baire function, so that ψ can be taken to be the latter type of function.

We conclude the proof by showing that a. e. $h(p) = \psi(k(p))$. It is evidently sufficient to show that $\int_E h(p)dr(p) = \int_E \psi(k(p))dr(p)$ for all $E \in \mathcal{R}$, but as every element of $\mathcal{R}$ differs by a null set from an element of $\mathcal{S}$, it is sufficient to establish the last equation for E of the form $k^{-1}(B)$, B being Borel. For such a set E, the equation is valid by the definition of ψ.

PART II.   NON-COMMUTATIVE ALGEBRAS.

7. <u>Decomposition theory</u>. In this section we obtain a decomposition of an arbitrary W*-algebra into parts of uniform multiplicity, and in the following section we determine the structure of the general W*-algebra of uniform finite multiplicity. Their structure for the case of infinite multiplicity remains, however, obscure, except in special cases.

The present decomposition coincides in the case of a commutative algebra with that obtained in Part I, but the method used in Part I is inappropriate in the non-commutative case, and the present method is not as well adapted to the abelian case as that of Part I. The basic difficulty in extending the method of Part I is that an algebra with a cyclic element need not be of uniform multiplicity one, in the non-commutative case, (with any reasonable definition of uniform multiplicity). The technique we employ here is in part an extension to the non-commutative case of a reformulation of the technique employed in $[6]$.

<u>Definitions 7.1</u>. A W*-algebra $\mathcal{A}$ on a Hilbert space $\mathcal{H}$ is said to be of <u>minimal multiplicity</u> <u>n</u> if n is the least upper bound of the cardinal numbers m such that there exist m mutually disjoint

projections P_μ in the commutor Q' of Q such that the operation of contracting Q to $P_\mu \mathcal{H}$ is an algebraic isomorphism. It is said to be of <u>uniform multiplicity</u> 0 if it consists only of the zero operator. It is said to be of <u>uniform multiplicity</u> <u>n</u> if for every nonzero projection P in the center of Q', the contraction of Q to $P\mathcal{H}$ has <u>minimal multiplicity</u> n.

THEOREM 6. <u>For any W*-algebra Q and each cardinal $n \geq 0$, there exists a projection P_n in the center of Q', such that the P_n are mutually orthogonal and have union equal to I, and with the contraction of Q to the range of P_n of uniform multiplicity n.</u>

LEMMA 6.1. <u>If the minimal multiplicity of a W*-algebra Q on $\mathcal{H}$ is $\geq n$, and if P is a nonzero projection in the center of Q', then the contraction of Q to the range of P is likewise of minimal multiplicity $\geq n$.</u>

Let $\{P_\mu\}$ be a family of mutually orthogonal projections in Q' such that the contracting of Q to $P_\mu \mathcal{H}$ is an isomorphism, for each μ. Then the PP_μ are mutually orthogonal projections in $(Q_P)'$, where Q_P is the contraction of Q to $P\mathcal{H}$, and the contracting of Q to $PP_\mu \mathcal{H}$ is an isomorphism, for if $T_P \in Q_P$, say T_P is the contraction of $T \in Q$, and $PP_\mu T_P = 0$, then it follows that $PP_\mu T = 0$, so $PT = 0$ and $T_P = 0$. The lemma follows now from the definition of minimal multiplicity.

LEMMA 6.2. <u>Let Q be a W*-algebra on $\mathcal{H}$ and $\{P_\mu\}$ be a family of mutually orthogonal projections in Q' such that the contraction of Q to the range of P_μ has minimal multiplicity $\geq n$, for all μ. Then the contraction of Q to the range of $\bigcup_\mu P_\mu$ likewise has minimal multiplicity $\geq n$.</u>

If m is any cardinal $\leq n$, then by the definition of the minimal multiplicity there exist projections $Q'_{\mu\nu}$, where ν ranges over a set of cardinality m, in $(Q_\mu)'$, where Q_μ is the contraction of Q to $P_\mu \mathcal{H}$, which are mutually orthogonal and such that the contracting of Q_μ to $Q'_{\mu\nu} P_\mu \mathcal{H}$ is an isomorphism. Now let $Q_{\mu\nu}$ be the unique projection orthogonal to $I - P_\mu$ whose contraction to $P_\mu \mathcal{H}$ is $Q'_{\mu\nu}$; it is not difficult to verify that $P_\mu Q_{\mu\nu} = Q_{\mu\nu}$ and that $Q_{\mu\nu} \in Q'$. Setting $R_\nu = \bigcup_\mu Q_{\mu\nu}$, then $R_\nu R_{\nu'} = 0$ if $\nu \neq \nu'$, for $Q_{\mu\nu} Q_{\mu'\nu'} = (Q_{\mu\nu} P_\nu)(P_{\nu'} Q_{\mu'\nu'}) = 0$ if $\nu \neq \nu'$, and it is not difficult to verify that if $\{A_\sigma\}$ and $\{B_\tau\}$ are families of projections on $\mathcal{H}$ such that $A_\sigma B_\tau = 0$ for any σ and τ, then $(\bigcup_\sigma A_\sigma)(\bigcup_\tau B_\tau) = 0$.

Thus $\{R_\nu\}$ is a family of m mutually orthogonal projections in Q'. To conclude the proof of the lemma it suffices to show that the contracting of Q_1 to $R_\nu \mathcal{H}$ is an isomorphism, where Q_1 is the contraction of Q to the range of $\bigcup_\mu P_\mu$. Now suppose that $R_\nu T = 0$ with $T \in Q_1$. Multiplying the last equation by $Q_{\mu\nu}$ shows that $Q_{\mu\nu} T = 0$, which implies that $Q_{\mu\nu} TP_\mu = 0$. As the contracting of Q_μ to $Q'_{\mu\nu} P_\mu \mathcal{H}$ is an isomorphism, it results that $TP_\mu = 0$. It is easy to deduce that $T = 0$.

LEMMA 6.3. <u>Let Q be a W*-algebra on $\mathcal{H}$ and $\{P_\mu\}$ a family of projections in the center of Q' such that the contraction of Q to the range of P_μ has minimal multiplicity $\geq n$, for all μ. Then the contraction of Q to the range of $\bigcup_\mu P_\mu$ likewise has minimal multiplicity $\geq n$.</u>

There is no essential loss of generality in assuming that the index set over which μ varies is well-ordered with first element 1. Defining $Q_\mu = P_\mu - \bigcup_{\nu<\mu} P_\nu$, for $\mu > 1$, and $Q_1 = P_1$, it is not difficult to verify that the Q_μ are mutually orthogonal, and that $Q_\mu \leq P_\mu$. It follows from Lemma 6.1 that the contraction of Q to $Q_\mu \mathcal{H}$ (which is the same as the contraction to $Q_\mu \mathcal{H}$ of the contraction of Q to $P_\mu \mathcal{H}$) has minimal multiplicity $\geq n$, and Lemma 6.2 now implies that the contraction of Q to $(\bigcup_\mu Q_\mu)\mathcal{H}$ has minimal multiplicity $\geq n$. The lemma now follows from the observation that $\bigcup_\mu Q_\mu = \bigcup_\mu P_\mu$.

LEMMA 6.4. _If_ Q _is a W*-algebra of_ _minimal multiplicity_ n _on_ $\mathcal{H}$, _then there exist mutually orthogonal projections_ P _and_ Q _in the center of_ Q' _such that the contraction of_ Q _to_ $P\mathcal{H}$ _is of uniform multiplicity_ n, _the contraction of_ Q _to_ $Q\mathcal{H}$ _is of minimal multiplicity greater than_ n, _and with sum_ P + Q _equal to the maximal projection in_ Q .

If Q is of uniform multiplicity n, then it is obvious that the conclusion is valid. Assuming that Q is not of uniform multiplicity n, let Q be the least upper bound of all projections R in the center of Q' such that the contraction of Q to $R\mathcal{H}$ is of minimal multiplicity $> n$. Then by Lemma 6.3, the contraction of Q to $Q\mathcal{H}$ has minimal multiplicity $> n$, and putting P $=$ E - Q, where E is the maximal projection in Q, it easily is seen that the contraction of Q to $P\mathcal{H}$ is of uniform multiplicity n.

PROOF OF THEOREM. We define the P_n by transfinite induction. We first put P_0 for the orthocomplement of the maximal projection E in Q. By Lemma 6.4, E $=$ P + Q where P and Q are mutually orthogonal projections in the center of Q, and with the contraction of Q to $Q\mathcal{H}$ of uniform multiplicity > 1; we set $P_1 = P$. Now suppose that P_m has been defined for m $<$ n in such a way that these are mutually orthogonal projections in the center of Q' with the properties that the contraction of $\mathcal{A}$ to $P_m \mathcal{H}$ is of uniform multiplicity m, and that the contraction of $\mathcal{A}$ to $(I - R_m)\mathcal{H}$ is of minimal multiplicity $> m$, where $R_m = \bigcup_{r \leq m} P_r$. Putting $N = \bigcup_{m<n} P_m$, then $I - N = \bigcup_{m<n} (I - P_m) = \bigcup_{m<n} (I - R_m)$, and by Lemma 6.1 the contraction of $\mathcal{A}$ to $(I - N)\mathcal{H}$ has minimal multiplicity $\geq n$. If $N = I$ we set $P_{n'} = 0$ for all $n' \geq n$; otherwise we take $P_n = P$, where P and Q are mutually orthogonal projections in the center of $\mathcal{A}'$ such that $P + Q = N$, and with the properties that the contractions of $\mathcal{A}$ to $P\mathcal{H}$ and to $Q\mathcal{H}$ are respectively of uniform multiplicity n and of minimal multiplicity $> n$ (the existence of P and Q being assured by Lemma 6.4). It is clear that in either case the hypothesis of the induction is valid at the next stage, so that the P_n are well-defined, and it is easily seen that they have the properties given in Theorem 6. (We note that the minimal multiplicity of the contraction of $\mathcal{A}$ to any invariant closed linear manifold is bounded from above by the cardinality of a set of mutually orthogonal projections in $\mathcal{A}'$, and hence by the dimension of $\mathcal{H}$).

We conclude this section by showing that the present notion of algebra of uniform multiplicity n agrees in the case of commutative algebras with the notion introduced in the first part of this paper.

THEOREM 7. __A commutative W*-algebra is of uniform multiplicity__ n __in the sense of Definition 2.1 if and only if it is of uniform multiplicity__ n __according to Definition 7.1.__

LEMMA 7.1. __If a commutative W*-algebra__ $\mathcal{A}$ __on__ $\mathcal{H}$ __is of uniform multiplicity__ n __in the sense of Definition 2.1 and of uniform multiplicity__ m __in the sense of Definition 7.1, then__ $m = n$.

It is clear from Definition 2.1 that there exist n mutually orthogonal projections P_i in $\mathcal{A}'$ such that the contracting of A to $P_i\mathcal{H}$ is an isomorphism, so $m \geq n$. Now suppose that $n \geq \aleph_o$. Let N

be a nonzero projection in $\mathcal{A}$ such that the contraction $\mathcal{A}_N$ of $\mathcal{A}$ to $N\mathcal{H}$ is countably-decomposable. Then N is in the center of $\mathcal{A}'$ so $\mathcal{A}_N$ is of uniform multiplicity n in the sense of Definition 2.1 and of uniform multiplicity m in the sense of Definition 7.1. It is clear that there exist n separating vectors $\{x_\mu\}$ for $\mathcal{A}_N$ such that $\mathcal{A}_N x_\mu$ is orthogonal to $\mathcal{A}_N x_{\mu'}$ for $\mu \neq \mu'$. Now assuming $m > n$, let $\{Q_\nu\}$ be a family of m' mutually orthogonal projections in $\mathcal{A}_N'$ where $m \geq m' > n$, such that the contracting of $\mathcal{A}_N$ to $Q_\nu (N\mathcal{H})$ is an isomorphism. The projection $x_{\mu\nu}$ of x_μ on $Q_\nu N\mathcal{H}$ vanishes except for countably many ν, so that the set of all indices ν for which $x_{\mu\nu} \neq 0$ for some μ has cardinality at most $\aleph_0 n$. However, for each ν there is a μ such that $x_{\mu\nu} \neq 0$, as otherwise, taking λ to be an index such that $x_{\mu\lambda} = 0$ for all μ, then clearly x_μ is orthogonal to $Q_\lambda N\mathcal{H}$ for all μ. In particular $(x_\mu, Ay_\lambda) = 0$ for all μ, all $A \in \mathcal{A}_N$ and all $y_\lambda \in Q_\lambda N\mathcal{H}$. It follows as in the proof of Lemma 2.9 that $y_\lambda = 0$, a contradiction. Hence $m \leq \aleph_0 n = n$, so $m = n$.

To conclude the proof of the lemma it suffices to show that if n is finite, then $m \leq n$. Let N and $\{Q_\nu\}$ be as in the preceding paragraph. Let y_ν be a separating vector for $\mathcal{A}_N$ in $Q_\nu N\mathcal{H}$. The remainder of the proof is essentially identical with the proof of Lemma 2.11, with y_ν playing the same role in both proofs.

PROOF OF THEOREM. Suppose to begin with that $\mathcal{A}$ on $\mathcal{H}$ is of uniform multiplicity n in the sense of Definition 2.1, where we may take $n \geq 1$, as the case $n = 0$ is trivial. Let $\{P_i\}$ be an indexed family of projections satisfying the conclusion of Theorem 2. Then the contraction of $\mathcal{A}$ to $P_i \mathcal{H}$ is of uniform multiplicity i in the sense of Definition 7.1 and of uniform multiplicity n in the sense of Definition 2.1, so $P_i = 0$ for $i \neq n$ by the preceding lemma (the algebra of all

transformations on a zero-dimensional space being taken to have uniform
multiplicity n, for all n) and it follows that Q is of uniform multiplicity in the sense of Definition 7.1.

Now assume that Q on H is of uniform multiplicity n in
the sense of Definition 7.1, where again we may take $n \geq 1$. Let $\{P_1\}$
be projections satisfying the conclusions of Theorem 2. Then the contraction of Q to $P_1 H$ is of uniform multiplicity i in the sense of Definition 7.1, so $P_1 = 0$ for $i \neq n$, and it follows that Q is of
uniform multiplicity n in the sense of either definition.

8. <u>Algebras</u> <u>of</u> <u>uniform</u> <u>multiplicity</u>. We show next that a W*-
algebra Q is of uniform multiplicity 1 if and only if Q' is commutative. The classification in Part I of commutative W*-algebras within
unitary equivalence thereby induces a similar classification of algebras
of uniform multiplicity 1. A W*-algebra of uniform finite multiplicity
n is shown to be an n-fold copy of an algebra of multiplicity 1. For infinite n the corresponding conclusion is not valid (as is clear from con-
sideration of the case of a factor of type II) and our results as regards
this case are highly incomplete, except that a basic special case is given
a full treatment in the next section. The commutative case of the next
theorem is due to Nakano $[7]$.

THEOREM 8. <u>A W*-algebra</u> <u>is</u> <u>of</u> <u>uniform</u> <u>multiplicity</u> <u>one</u> <u>if</u> <u>and</u>
<u>only</u> <u>if</u> <u>its</u> <u>commutor</u> <u>is</u> <u>commutative</u>.

Let Q be of uniform multiplicity 1 on H, so $I \in Q$.
Clearly Q' is commutative if and only if $Q' \subset Q$, and this in turn
is the case provided Q contains all projections in Q'. Now let P
be an arbitrary projection in Q', let R be the L.U.B. of all projections Q in Q such that QP = 0, and let S be the L.U.B. of the
projections Q in Q for which QP = Q. It is easily seen that

RP $=$ 0 and SP $=$ S, so RS $=$ R(PS) $=$ (RP)S $=$ 0. Now if U is an arbitrary unitary operator in $\mathcal{Q}$, the equation QP $=$ 0 implies that U*QPU $=$ 0 $=$ (U*QU)P. It follows that R $=$ U*RU, i. e., R is in the center of $\mathcal{Q}$. Similarly S is in the center of $\mathcal{Q}$.

Now I - R $\geq$ P(I - R) $=$ P $\geq$ PS $=$ S, so I - R $\geq$ P $\geq$ S. By the definition of uniform multiplicity, with I - R - S $=$ 0, in which case the preceding inequality shows that P $\in$ $\mathcal{Q}$, or the contraction $\mathcal{Q}_1$ of $\mathcal{Q}$ to the range of I - R - S is of uniform multiplicity 1. We show that the latter alternative is an impossibility.

We show first that the contracting of $\mathcal{Q}_1$ to P(I - R - S)$\mathcal{H}$ is an isomorphism, i. e., that if U $\in$ $\mathcal{Q}_1$ and if P(I - R - S)U $=$ 0, then (I - R - S)U $=$ 0. Now it is sufficient to show this for the case when U is a projection. To see this, let N $=$ P(I - R - S), so NU $=$ 0 and NUU* $=$ 0. Clearly Nf(UU*) $=$ 0 for any polynomial f such that f(0) $=$ 0, and hence if K is any projection in the W*-algebra generated by UU*, NK $=$ 0. As this algebra is generated by the projections it contains, the equation NK $=$ 0 for all K implies that NUU* $=$ 0 $=$ (NU)(NU)*, so NU $=$ 0. Now taking U to be a projection in $\mathcal{Q}$, suppose that P(I - R - S)U $=$ 0. Then (I - R - S)U $\leq$ R, by the definition of R, and multiplying this inequality by I - R - S (which commutes with both sides) yields the inequality (I - R - S)U $\leq$ 0, so (I - R - S)U $=$ 0.

Next we show that the contracting of $\mathcal{Q}_1$ to (I - P)(I - R - S)$\mathcal{H}$ is also an isomorphism. As in the preceding paragraph, it is sufficient to show that if U is a projection in $\mathcal{Q}$ such that (I - P)(I - R - S)U $=$ 0, then (I - R - S)U $=$ 0. The equation (I - P)(I - R - S)U $=$ 0 can be put in the form P(I - R - S)U $=$ (I - R - S)U, which by the definition of S implies that (I - R - S)U $\leq$ S. Multiplying both sides of this inequality by I - R - S shows that (I - R - S)U $=$ 0. Now the projections P(I - R - S) and (I - P)(I - R - S) are obviously orthogonal, so what has just been proved shows that Q_1 is of minimal multiplicity at least 2, a contradiction. Hence the second alternative above was impossible.

Now suppose conversely that Q' is commutative, so $Q' \subset Q$. If Q is not of uniform multiplicity 1, then for some nonzero projection P in the center Q' of Q, the contraction Q_1 of Q to PH is of minimal multiplicity at least 2. Suppose then that Q_1' and Q_2' are mutually orthogonal projections in $(Q_1)'$ such that the contracting of Q_1 to $Q_i' PH$ is an isomorphism (i = 1,2). Let Q_1 and Q_2 be the unique projections on H which coincide on PH with Q_1' and Q_2' and which annihilate the orthogonal complement of PH. Then Q_1 and Q_2 are in Q', for if T is arbitrary in Q, then taking the case of Q_1 we have (noting that $Q_1 P = P Q_1 = Q_1$) $Q_1 T = (Q_1 P)T = Q_1(PT) = Q_1(PTP)$ (for P is in the center of Q) = $(PTP)Q_1$ (as $Q_1' \in (Q_1)'$) = $(TP)Q_1 = T(PQ_1) = TQ_1$. Therefore Q_1 and Q_2 are in Q, and as Q_1' and Q_2' are mutually orthogonal, $(Q_1 P)(Q_2 P) = 0$, which shows that the contracting of Q_1 to $Q_1 PH$ annihilates $Q_2 P$, and so is not an isomorphism.

Algebras of uniform multiplicity 1 play a conspicuous role in the following, and so it is convenient to make the following definition, which is justified by the fact that a W*-algebra containing I is of uniform multiplicity 1 if and only if the lattice of all closed linear subspaces invariant under the algebra is a Boolean algebra.

Definition 8.1. An algebra of operators is called <u>hyper-reducible</u> if it is a W*-algebra of uniform multiplicity 1.

COROLLARY 8.1. <u>If two hyper-reducible algebras are algebraically isomorphic, then they are unitarily equivalent.</u>

Let the hyper-reducible algebras Q_1 and Q_2 on Hilbert spaces H_1 and H_2 be algebraically isomorphic via the map φ on Q_1

to Q_2. Then φ maps the center C_1 of Q_1 isomorphically onto the center C_2 of Q_2. Let M_1 be any masa algebra on H_1 which contains C_1. As Q_1 is hyper-reducible, $C_1 = (Q_1)'$, so $(C_1)' = (Q_1)'' = Q_1$, and hence $M_1 \subset Q_1$. Putting $M_2 = \varphi(M_1)$, then M_2 is masa on H_2, for as φ is an algebraic isomorphism, M_2 is maximal abelian relative to Q_2, i. e., $(M_2)' \cap Q_2 = M_2$. Taking commutors, it follows that $M_2 \cup Q_2' = (M_2)'$, and as $(Q_2)' = C_2 \subset M_2$, it results that $M_2 = (M_2)'$, i. e., M_2 is masa. We can now apply the result in $[10]$ that if two masa algebras on Hilbert spaces are algebraically isomorphic, then there is a unitary transformation U between the spaces which implements the isomorphism. As C_1 is carried onto C_2 by the operator-isomorphism induced by U, $(C_1)'$ is carried onto $(C_2)'$ by that isomorphism, i. e., Q_1 is mapped onto Q_2.

COROLLARY 8.2. **A W*-algebra of finite uniform multiplicity** $n > 0$ **is unitarily equivalent to an n-fold copy of a hyper-reducible algebra, the latter algebra being unique within unitary equivalence.**

Let Q be a W*-algebra on H of finite uniform multiplicity n, and let $P_1, \ldots, P_n$ be an indexed set of n mutually orthogonal projections in Q' such that for each i, the contracting of Q to $P_i H$ is an isomorphism. We show first that the contraction Q_1 of Q to $P_i H$ is hyper-reducible. Let Q' be a nonzero projection in the center of Q_1, and let Q be the projection in Q of which Q' is the contraction. As the basis of an indirect proof suppose that the contraction B of Q_1 to $Q'P_i H$ has minimal multiplicity ≥ 2 (for some fixed i), so that there exist projections R' and S' on $Q'P_i H$ in B', mutually orthogonal, and such that the contractings of B to $R'Q'P_i H$ and to $S'Q'P_i H$ are isomorphisms. Putting R and S for the projections on QH which agree on $Q'P_i H$ with R' and S' respectively, and which annihilate

$Q(I-P_1)\mathcal{H}$, then it is not difficult to verify that R and S are in $\mathcal{C}'$, where $\mathcal{C}$ is the contraction of $\mathcal{Q}$ to $Q\mathcal{H}$, that R and S are mutually orthogonal, and that the contractings of $\mathcal{C}$ to $RQ\mathcal{H}$ and to $SQ\mathcal{H}$ are both isomorphisms. Now the contractings of $\mathcal{C}$ to $P_jQ\mathcal{H}$ $(j \neq 1)$ are likewise isomorphisms and the contractions of P_j to $Q\mathcal{H}$ $(j \neq 1)$, R and S, together constitute a set of $n + 1$ mutually orthogonal projections in $\mathcal{C}$. It follows that $\mathcal{C}$ is of minimal multiplicity at least $n + 1$, but Q is in the center of $\mathcal{Q}$, so this is in contradiction with the definition of uniform multiplicity, which requires that $\mathcal{C}$ be of uniform multiplicity n.

By Corollary 8.1, there is a hyper-reducible algebra $\mathcal{B}$ such that each $\mathcal{Q}_i$ is unitarily equivalent to $\mathcal{B}$. It is straightforward to show that $\mathcal{Q}$ is unitarily equivalent to an n-fold copy of $\mathcal{B}$.

The final theorem in this section concerns the uniqueness of multiplicities in the non-commutative case.

THEOREM 9. **An m-fold copy of a hyper-reducible algebra $\mathcal{D}$ is unitarily equivalent to an n-fold copy of a hyper-reducible algebra $\mathcal{E}$ if and only if m = n and $\mathcal{D}$ and $\mathcal{E}$ are unitarily equivalent.**

As the "if" part is clear, we assume that the W*-algebra $\mathcal{Q}$ on $\mathcal{H}$ is unitarily equivalent to an m-fold copy of $\mathcal{D}$ and also to an n-fold copy of $\mathcal{E}$. Then $\mathcal{Q}$ is algebraically isomorphic to both $\mathcal{D}$ and $\mathcal{E}$, so that $\mathcal{D}$ and $\mathcal{E}$ are algebraically isomorphic, and hence (by Corollary 8.1) unitarily equivalent. We can now assume that $\mathcal{D} = \mathcal{E}$; for each $T \in \mathcal{D}$, let $\varphi(T)$ and $\psi(T)$ be the unitary transforms in $\mathcal{Q}$ of the m- and n-fold copies of T, respectively. Now let $\mathcal{M}$ be a masa subalgebra of $\mathcal{D}$ (the existence of which is shown in the proof of Corollary 8.1), let $\varphi(\mathcal{M}) = \mathcal{C}$, and let $\psi^{-1}(\mathcal{C}) = \mathcal{N}$. Then $\mathcal{N}$ is maximal abelian and SA in $\mathcal{D}$, as φ and ψ are algebraic isomorphisms, and hence masa (cf. the proof of Corollary 8.1). It follows that $\mathcal{M}$ and $\mathcal{N}$ are unitarily equivalent [10] . As $\mathcal{C}$ is unitarily equivalent both to an m-fold copy of $\mathcal{M}$ and to an n-fold copy of $\mathcal{N}$, it results from Lemmas 2.9 and 2.11 that $m = n$.

COROLLARY 9.1. Let $\{P_n'\}$ be a family of projections in the center of the W*-algebra $\mathcal{Q}$ on $\mathcal{H}$ indexed by cardinal numbers n, such that for each n the contraction of $\mathcal{Q}$ to the range of P_n' has uniform multiplicity n, and $\bigcup_n P_n' = I$. Then if $\{P_n\}$ is a family with the property given in Theorem 6, for all finite n $P_n = P_n'$ (so that if $\mathcal{H}$ is separable, this equation is valid for all n).

LEMMA 9.1.1. If $\mathcal{Q}$ is a W*-algebra on $\mathcal{H}$, and if R and S are projections in the center of A such that the contractions of $\mathcal{Q}$ to $R\mathcal{H}$ and $S\mathcal{H}$ have uniform multiplicities m and n respectively, where $m \neq n$ and at least one of m and n is finite, then $RS = 0$.

Clearly the contraction of $\mathcal{Q}$ to $RS\mathcal{H}$ has uniform multiplicities both m and n, and if these are both finite, it follows directly from Theorem 9 and Corollary 8.2 that $RS = 0$. Now let n be finite and m infinite, and suppose that $RS \neq 0$. Then the contraction $\mathcal{Q}_0$ of $\mathcal{Q}$ to $RS\mathcal{H}$ is unitarily equivalent to an n-fold copy of a hyper-reducible algebra $\mathcal{D}$. Let $\mathcal{M}$ be a masa subalgebra of $\mathcal{D}$, let φ be the algebraic isomorphism of $\mathcal{D}$ onto $\mathcal{Q}_0$ induced by the map of $\mathcal{D}$ onto its n-fold copy and by the unitary equivalence of this copy with $\mathcal{Q}_0$, and set $\varphi(\mathcal{M}) = \mathcal{N}$, so that $\mathcal{N}$ is unitarily equivalent to an n-fold copy of $\mathcal{M}$. Now as $\mathcal{Q}$ is of infinite uniform multiplicity, there exist mutually orthogonal projections $P_1, P_2, \ldots$ in $\mathcal{Q}'$ such that for each i the map $T \longrightarrow P_1 T$ is an isomorphism on $\mathcal{Q}$. As $\mathcal{Q} \supset \mathcal{N}$, $\mathcal{Q}' \subset \mathcal{N}'$, so that the P_1 are in $\mathcal{N}'$, and clearly the map $T \longrightarrow P_1 T$ is an isomorphism on $\mathcal{N}$. Thus $\mathcal{N}$ is of minimal multiplicity $\aleph_0$. On the other hand, it

is of uniform multiplicity n according to Definition 2.1, hence of uniform multiplicity n according to Definition 7.1, so that it cannot be of
minimal multiplicity $\aleph_o$.

PROOF OF COROLLARY. Let P_n be the L.U.B. of all projections Q
in the center of Q such that Q has uniform multiplicity n on $Q\mathcal{H}$,
by Lemma 6.3, Q has uniform multiplicity n on $P_n\mathcal{H}$. Let $P_\infty =$
$\bigcup_{n \geq \aleph_o} P_n$ and $P'_\infty = \bigcup_{n \geq \aleph_o} P'_n$. Evidently $P'_n \leq P_n$ for all n and
$P'_\infty \leq P_\infty$. By the preceding lemma, the P_n with finite n are mutually
orthogonal, and are also orthogonal to the P_m with infinite m, and hence
orthogonal to P_∞ . As $(\bigcup_{n < \aleph_o} P'_n) \cup P'_\infty = I = (\bigcup_{n < \aleph_o} P_n) \cup P_\infty$,
we have $P'_n = P_n$ for $n < \aleph_o$ and $P'_\infty = P_\infty$. Finally, if $\mathcal{H}$ is
separable, it is plain that necessarily $P'_n = 0$ for $n > \aleph_o$.

9. <u>Algebras</u> <u>of</u> <u>type</u> <u>I</u>. We give a structure theorem for W*-alge-
bras of "type I", where these are, roughly speaking, algebras which are
direct integrals of factors of type I. At the same time we obtain a complete set of unitary invariants for such algebras, which can be regarded as
fully known by virtue of this classification. The following definition of
algebra of type I is equivalent to a definition in [1] for certain abstract algebras.

<u>Definition 9.1</u>. A W*-algebra is said to be of <u>type I</u> if every
projection in Q' is the least upper bound of projections of type M in
Q', where a projection P in Q' is of <u>type M</u> if whenever Q is a projection in Q' such that $Q \leq P$, then $Q = RP$ where R is a projection
in $Q \cap Q'$.

Roughly speaking, a projection P is of type M if when the algebra is decomposed as a direct integral of factors, P decomposes into an
integral of projections each of which has a range which is of (ordinary
linear) dimension at most one, so that it is akin to a minimal projection,

as our terminology is intended to suggest. The following theorem asserts essentially that a W*-algebra is of type I if and only if it is a direct sum of n-fold copies of hyper-reducible algebras.

THEOREM 10. A W*-algebra Q on H is of type I if and only if there exists a family $\{P_n\}$ of projections in the center of Q', indexed by cardinal numbers n, which are mutually orthogonal and have union I, and are such that the contraction of Q to $P_n H$ (n > 0) is unitarily equivalent to an n-fold copy of a hyper-reducible algebra D_n of uniform multiplicity n, while $I-P_0$ is the maximal projection in Q.

The P_n are unique as are, within unitary equivalence, the D_n. Conversely Q is determined within unitary equivalence by the knowledge of the D_n as abstract algebras (which knowledge determines the D_n within unitary equivalence), or alternatively by the unitary invariants of the commutative algebras D_n', together with the dimension of the range of P_0.

Remark 9.1. Naturally a second alternative to the D_n as unitary invariants are the invariants of the D_n' as given in Part I. This implies that a cardinal-valued function F(n,m,p) of triples of cardinal numbers could also be used in place of the unitary-equivalence classes of the D_n. Here F(n,m,p) is the cardinality of the number of summands isomorphic to the measure ring of the product measure space I^p (where I is the unit interval under Lebesgue measure) which occur in a decomposition into finite homogeneous parts of the measure ring for multiplicity m of D_n', and it is necessary as earlier to normalize F(n,m,p), say by setting it equal to 1 for the case when $p \neq 0$ and the number F of summands is determined only within the interval $1 \leq F \leq \aleph_0$, and I^0 must be suitably interpreted. Clearly any cardinal-valued function F(n,m,p) which vanishes for sufficiently large n, m, and p, then corresponds to a unique

unitary equivalence class of W*-algebras of type I containing the identity
operator.

The first six of the following lemmas are needed in the proof of
the "only if" part of the theorem, while the remaining lemmas are for the
"if" part.

LEMMA 10.1. <u>Let</u> T <u>be a non-negative SA operator in the W*-alge-
bra</u> $\mathcal{A}$, <u>and suppose that</u> $T \leq P$ <u>and</u> $PT = TP = T$, <u>where</u> P <u>is a projection of type M in</u> $\mathcal{A}$. <u>Then there exists an operator</u> S <u>in the center
of</u> $\mathcal{A}$ <u>such that</u> $T = SP$ <u>and</u> $0 \leq S \leq I$.

The W*-algebra $\mathcal{C}$ generated by P and T is obviously commutative and has a unit, and so is isomorphic to the algebra $\mathcal{C}(\Gamma)$ of all
continuous functions on a compact Hausdorff space Γ. It follows without
difficulty that there exist projections Q_{in} in $\mathcal{C}$ and real numbers α_{in}
$(i, n = 1, 2, \ldots)$ such that for each fixed n, the Q_{in} are mutually
orthogonal, the α_{in} satisfy the inequalities $0 < \alpha_{in} < 1$, and with
$T_n \longrightarrow T$ uniformly where $T_n = \sum_i \alpha_{in} Q_{in}$ and $T_n \leq T_{n+1}$. Evidently
$Q_{in} \leq P$ so that $Q_{in} = R_{in}P$ with R_{in} a projection in $\mathcal{A} \cap \mathcal{A}'$, and
$T_n = (\sum_i \alpha_{in} R_{in})P$ or $T_n = R_n P$ with $R_n \in \mathcal{A} \cap \mathcal{A}'$. Now let S_n
be the G. L. B. of all such non-negative operators R_n; then clearly $T_n =
S_n P$. Now $S_n \leq S_{n+1}$ for denoting lattice intersection in the set of SA
elements in $\mathcal{C}$ by "$\wedge$", we have $T_n = T_n \wedge T_{n+1} = S_n P \wedge S_{n+1} P =
(S_n \wedge S_{n+1})P$ (noting that $S_n P = S_n \wedge P$) which shows that $S_n \wedge S_{n+1} =
S_n$, by the minimality of S_n, or $S_n \leq S_{n+1}$. It follows that $\{S_n\}$ con-
verges strongly to an operator S in $A \cap A'$ and $T = SP$; as it is easily seen that $0 \leq S_n \leq I$, we have $0 \leq S \leq I$.

LEMMA 10.2. <u>Any projection of type M in a W*-algebra is contained
in a maximal projection of type M.</u>

This follows at once from Zorn's principle once it is shown that the L. U. B. of any chain of projections of type M is again of type M. Now if $\mathcal{F}$ is such a chain in the W*-algebra $\mathcal{C}$, and Q is the L. U. B. of the elements of $\mathcal{F}$, suppose that A is a projection in $\mathcal{C}$ such that $A \leq Q$. To conclude the proof of the lemma it is only necessary to show that $A = RQ$ for some R in $\mathcal{C} \cap \mathcal{C}'$. Now for any $P \in \mathcal{F}$ we have $PAP \leq PQP = P$. It follows from the preceding lemma that $PAP = R_P P$ for some operator R_P in $\mathcal{C} \cap \mathcal{C}'$ such that $0 \leq R_P \leq I$. Putting S_P for the G. L. B. of all such R_P, then clearly $PAP = S_P P$, and S_P is a monotone increasing function of P, for if $P_i \in \mathcal{F}$ (i = 1,2) and $P_1 \geq P_2$, then $P_2 P_1 A P_1 P_2 = P_2 S_{P_1} A P_2$ or $P_2 A P_2 = S_{P_1} P_2$ which implies $S_{P_2} \leq S_{P_1}$. Now let S be the L. U. B. of the S_P, $P \in \mathcal{F}$. Then S is the strong limit of the $\{S_P\}$ where this indexed set is directed by the usual ordering on the indices, and passing to the limit in the equation $PAP = S_P P$ yields the equation $QAQ = SQ$, or $A = SQ$.

LEMMA 10.3. *If* P *and* Q *are projections of type M in the W*-algebra* $\mathcal{C}$*, and if* R *and* S *are mutually orthogonal projections in* $\mathcal{C} \cap \mathcal{C}'$*, then* $RP + SQ$ *is also of type M in* $\mathcal{C}$*.*

Suppose that E is a projection in $\mathcal{C}$ such that $E \leq RP + SQ$. Then $E \leq R + S$ so $E = ER + ES$, and $ER \leq RP$ so $ER = R'RP$ with $R' \in \mathcal{C} \cap \mathcal{C}'$. Similarly $ES = S'SQ$ with $S' \in \mathcal{C} \cap \mathcal{C}'$. Thus $E = R'RP + S'SQ = (RR' + SS')(RP + SQ)$.

LEMMA 10.4. *If* $\mathcal{Q}$ *is a W*-algebra of type I on* $\mathcal{H}$ *and if* $\mathcal{L}$ *is any closed linear subspace invariant under* $\mathcal{Q}$*, then the contraction of* $\mathcal{Q}$ *to* $\mathcal{L}$ *is again of type I.*

Let $\mathcal{Q}_1$ be the contraction of $\mathcal{Q}$ to $\mathcal{L}$ and let P_1 be a nonzero projection in $(\mathcal{Q}_1)'$. Let P be the projection on $\mathcal{H}$ which extends P_1 and annihilates $\mathcal{H} \ominus \mathcal{L}$. Then $P \in \mathcal{Q}'$ for if $U \in \mathcal{Q}$, we have for $x \in \mathcal{L}$, $UPx = Ux = PUx$, and for $x \in \mathcal{H} \ominus \mathcal{L}$, $UPx = 0 = PUx$, so $UP = PU$. Let Q be any nonzero projection of type M in $\mathcal{Q}'$ such that $Q \leq P$. Then Q annihilates $\mathcal{H} \ominus \mathcal{L}$, so it leaves $\mathcal{L}$ invariant; let Q_1 be its contraction to $\mathcal{L}$. Then $Q_1 \in (\mathcal{Q}_1)'$ for if $U_1 \in \mathcal{Q}_1$, say U_1 is the contraction of $U \in \mathcal{Q}$, then we have for $x \in \mathcal{L}$, $Q_1 U_1 x = QUx = UQx = U_1 Q_1 x$. Also it is clear that $Q_1 \leq P_1$. Finally Q_1 is of type M for if S_1 is a projection in $(\mathcal{Q}_1)'$, then S_1 is the contraction to $\mathcal{L}$ of the projection S in $\mathcal{Q}'$ where $S(\mathcal{H} \ominus \mathcal{L}) = 0$, and the equation $S_1 \leq Q_1$ implies that $S \leq Q$; and as Q is of type M, it results that $S = RQ$ with $R \in \mathcal{Q} \cap \mathcal{Q}'$, from which it results that $S_1 = R_1 Q_1$ with $R_1 \in \mathcal{Q}_1 \cap (\mathcal{Q}_1)'$.

LEMMA 10.5. *Let* $\mathcal{Q}$ *be a W*-algebra on* $\mathcal{H}$ *of type* I, *and let* P *be a maximal projection of type* M *in* $\mathcal{Q}'$. *Then the contracting of* $\mathcal{Q}$ *to* $P\mathcal{H}$ *is an isomorphism.*

It is sufficient, by a remark in Part I, to show that if S is a projection in $\mathcal{Q}$ such that $PS = 0$, then $S = 0$. Now let T be the L. U. B. of all the projections S in $\mathcal{Q}$ such that $SP = 0$. If $SP = 0$ and U is unitary in $\mathcal{Q}$, then $U*(SP)U = 0$ so that $(U*SU)P = 0$. Thus T is the L. U. B. of a set of projections which is invariant under the inner automorphisms induced by the unitary operators in $\mathcal{Q}$, and hence is in the center of $\mathcal{Q}$. If Q is a projection in $\mathcal{Q}'$ of type M and such that $T \geq Q$, then by Lemma 10.3, $P(I-T) + QT = P + Q$ is again of type M. By the maximality of P, $Q = 0$, and since T is the L. U. B. of such Q, it follows that $T = 0$.

LEMMA 10.6. *If* $\mathcal{Q}$ *is a nonzero W*-algebra on* $\mathcal{H}$ *of type* I, *then there exists a nonzero projection* P *in* $\mathcal{Q} \cap \mathcal{Q}'$ *such that the contraction of* $\mathcal{Q}$ *to* $P\mathcal{H}$ *is unitarily equivalent to an n-fold copy of a* hyper-reducible algebra, for some cardinal n > 0.

Let $\mathcal{F}$ be an indexed family of projections P_μ in $\mathcal{A}'$ which is maximal with respect to the properties: 1) for each μ the contracting of $\mathcal{A}$ to $P_\mu \mathcal{H}$ is an isomorphism; 2) the P_μ are mutually orthogonal; 3) each P_μ is of type M (the existence of $\mathcal{F}$ is clear from Lemmas 10.2 and 10.5). Let Q_0 be the L. U. B. of the projections Q in $\mathcal{A}$ for which $Q(I - \bigcup_\mu P_\mu) = 0$. Then $Q_0 \neq 0$, as otherwise $I - \bigcup_\mu P_\mu \neq 0$, and the contracting of $\mathcal{A}$ to $(I - \bigcup_\mu P_\mu)\mathcal{H}$ is an isomorphism. In continuation of this argument, let $\mathcal{A}_1$ on $\mathcal{H}_1$ be this contraction; by Lemma 10.4, $\mathcal{A}_1$ is of type I. Let Q_1 be a maximal projection in $(\mathcal{A}_1)'$ of type M, and let Q be the projection on $\mathcal{H}$ (necessarily in $\mathcal{A}'$) which extends Q_1 and annihilates $\mathcal{H} \ominus \mathcal{H}_1$. Then the contracting of $\mathcal{A}$ to $Q\mathcal{H}$ ($= Q_1 \mathcal{H}_1$) is an isomorphism, Q is orthogonal to all the P_μ, and it follows as in the proof of Lemma 10.4 that Q is of type M. This contradicts the maximality of $\mathcal{F}$ and so shows that $Q_0 \neq 0$.

By an argument used in the proof of Lemma 10.5, Q_0 is in the center of $\mathcal{A}$. Putting $P_\mu' = Q_0 P_\mu$ and $K_\mu = P_\mu' \mathcal{H}$, then: (a) $\mathcal{A}$ leaves $\mathcal{K}_\mu$ invariant and its contraction $\mathcal{A}_\mu$ to $\mathcal{K}_\mu$ is of type I; (b) the identity in $(\mathcal{A}_\mu)'$ (i.e. the contraction of P_μ' to $\mathcal{K}_\mu$) is of type M in $(\mathcal{A}_\mu)'$ (by an argument used in the proof of Lemma 10.4); (c) the contracting to $\mathcal{K}_\mu$ of the contraction of $\mathcal{A}$ to $Q_0 \mathcal{H}$ is an isomorphism. It is clear that the identity operator is of type M in a W*-algebra only if the algebra is commutative, and hence the $\mathcal{A}_\mu$ are hyper-reducible. If n is the cardinality of the index set, it follows from Corollary 8.1 that the contraction of $\mathcal{A}$ to $Q_0 \mathcal{H}$ ($= \bigcup_\mu \mathcal{K}_\mu$) is unitarily equivalent to an n-fold copy of any one of the $\mathcal{A}_\mu$.

LEMMA 10.7.   **A commutative W*-algebra is of type I.**

Let $\mathcal{A}$ be a commutative nonzero W*-algebra on $\mathcal{H}$. To show that $\mathcal{A}$ is of type I it suffices to show that for any projection P in $\mathcal{A}'$, there is a projection of type M in $\mathcal{A}'$ which is contained in P. Let W be a countably-decomposable projection in $\mathcal{A}$ such that WP $\neq$ 0 (cf. Lemma 2.7), let V be the maximal projection in $\mathcal{A}$ such that VWP = 0, and put $\mathcal{A}_1$ for the contraction of $\mathcal{A}$ to $\mathcal{H}_1 = (I-V)W\mathcal{H}$. As $\mathcal{A}_1$ is countably-decomposable and as the contracting of $\mathcal{A}_1$ to $P\mathcal{H}_1$ is an isomorphism, there exists a separating vector x_1 for A_1 in $P\mathcal{H}_1$. Putting $\{x_\mu\}$ for an indexed family of separating vectors for $\mathcal{A}_1$ which is maximal with respect to the properties that it contains x_1, and that $\mathcal{A}x_\mu$ is orthogonal to Ax_ν for $\mu \neq \nu$, a repetition of the construction at the beginning of the proof of Lemma 2.6 shows that there exists a nonzero projection Q_1 in $\mathcal{A}_1$ such that if $\mathcal{A}_2$ is the contraction of $\mathcal{A}_1$ to $Q_1\mathcal{H}_1$, and if R_μ is the projection of $Q_1\mathcal{H}_1$ onto the closure of $\mathcal{A}_2x_\mu$, then $Q_1 = \bigcup_\mu R_\mu$ and the contraction of $\mathcal{A}_2$ to $R_\mu\mathcal{H}$ is masa, $\mathcal{A}_2$ being unitarily equivalent to an n-fold copy of this masa algebra, where n is the cardinality of the index set. Putting S for the projection of $\mathcal{H}$ onto $R_1Q_1\mathcal{H}_1$ then it is easily seen that S $\leq$ P, and we conclude the proof of the lemma by showing that S is of type M in $\mathcal{A}'$. Let Q_0 be a projection in $\mathcal{A}$ whose contraction to $\mathcal{H}_1$ is Q_1, and set Q = $(I-V)WQ_0$, so Q $\in \mathcal{A}$ and $Q\mathcal{H} = Q_1\mathcal{H}_1$. Now $\mathcal{A}$ leaves $R_1\mathcal{H}$ invariant, for if U is arbitrary in $\mathcal{A}$, U = UQ + U(I-Q), and UQ leaves $R_1\mathcal{H}$ invariant because its contraction to $Q\mathcal{H}$ is in $\mathcal{A}_2$ while U(I-Q) annihilates $R_1\mathcal{H}$; therefore S $\in \mathcal{A}'$. Finally if T is any projection in $\mathcal{A}'$ such that T $\leq$ S, then the contraction T_1 of T to $Q\mathcal{H}$ is in $\mathcal{A}_2'$ and T' $\leq R_1$. As $\mathcal{A}_2$ is masa on $R_1\mathcal{H}$ and leaves $T_1Q_1\mathcal{H}$ invariant, $T_1 = R_1U_1$ with $U_1 \in \mathcal{A}_2 \cap (\mathcal{A}_2)'$, and putting U_0 for a projection in $\mathcal{A}$ whose contraction to $Q\mathcal{H}$ is U_1 and U = QU_0, it is not difficult to verify that T = UR, and U $\in \mathcal{A} \cap \mathcal{A}'$, for U $\in \mathcal{A}$ and $\mathcal{A}$ is commutative.

LEMMA 10.8. _Let the W*-algebra_ $\mathcal{A}$ _be an n-fold copy of a hyper-reducible algebra. Then_ $\mathcal{A}$ _is of type_ I.

It is easily seen that if $\{P_n\}$ is an indexed family of mutually orthogonal projections in the center of a W*-algebra $\mathcal{A}$ such that the contraction of $\mathcal{A}$ to the range of P_n is of type I and with $\bigcup_n P_n = I$, then $\mathcal{A}$ is itself of type I. It follows without difficulty from Theorem 2 that it suffices to consider the case in which the hyper-reducible algebra $\mathcal{B}$ of which $\mathcal{A}$ is an n-fold copy has its commutor equal to an m-fold copy of a masa algebra $\mathcal{M}$ on $\mathcal{H}$.

Let $\mathcal{A}$ act on $\mathcal{H}$, $\mathcal{B}$ act on $\mathcal{L}$, and let $\{\mathcal{L}_\mu\}$ be the copies of $\mathcal{L}$ which are (mutually orthogonal) subspaces of $\mathcal{H}$. If T is any operator on $\mathcal{H}$ and P_μ is the projection on $\mathcal{L}_\mu$, then $P_\nu T P_\mu$ maps $\mathcal{L}_\mu$ into $\mathcal{L}_\nu$ and so induces in a natural fashion an operator $T_{\mu\nu}$ on $\mathcal{L}$; by the matrix of T we mean this matrix $((T_{\mu\nu}))$, which is a function on the direct product of the index set with itself to the operators on $\mathcal{L}$. It is not difficult to verify that a matrix $((S_{\mu\nu}))$ is the matrix of an operator in $\mathcal{A}'$ if and only if: (1) it is the matrix of a bounded operator, i. e., if x is arbitrary in $\mathcal{H}$, if x^μ is the corresponding element of $\mathcal{L}_\mu$ and x_μ the element of $\mathcal{L}$ corresponding to x^μ, then the sum $\sum_\mu S_{\mu\nu} x_\mu$ is convergent (this is the case if and only if $\|S_{\mu\nu}\|$ is bounded for each fixed ν as a function of μ) and $\sum_\nu \|\sum_\mu S_{\mu\nu} x_\mu\|^2$ is a convergent sum; (2) $S_{\mu\nu} \in \mathcal{B}'$ for each μ, ν. We omit the details of the verification of this, as they involve standard methods.

Now let φ be the algebraic isomorphism of $\mathcal{B}'$ onto $\mathcal{M}$ which takes each operator into the operator of which is the m-fold copy. Let $\mathcal{N}$ on $\mathcal{G}$ be the n-fold copy of $\mathcal{M}$ on $\mathcal{K}$. If $S \in \mathcal{A}'$, and $((S_{\mu\nu}))$ is the matrix of S, then $S_{\mu\nu} \in \mathcal{B}'$ and $((\varphi(S_{\mu\nu})))$ is a matrix of operators in $\mathcal{M}$; we shall show that is the matrix of an operator $\Phi(S)$ in $\mathcal{N}'$ (relative to the decomposition of the space $\mathcal{G}$ on which $\mathcal{N}$ acts as an n-fold direct sum of copies of $\mathcal{K}$), and that Φ is an algebraic isomorphism onto. To show that $((\phi(S_{\mu\nu})))$ is the matrix of an operator in $\mathcal{N}$, it is only necessary to check condition (1) above. Now each $\mathcal{L}_\mu$ is in a natural fashion an m-fold direct sum of copies $\mathcal{L}_{\mu\sigma}$ of $\mathcal{K}$. For each μ, let σ_1 be any index in the range of values of σ, and for each y in $\mathcal{G}$ let y_μ be the element of $\mathcal{K}$ corresponding to the projection of y on the μth copy of $\mathcal{K}$ in $\mathcal{G}$, and further let $\eta(y)$ be that element x in $\mathcal{H}$ such that $x_{\mu\sigma_1} = y_\mu$ and $x_{\mu\sigma} = 0$ if $\sigma \neq \sigma_1$, where $x_{\mu\sigma}$ is the element in $\mathcal{K}$ corresponding to the projection of x on the σth copy of $\mathcal{K}$ in the μth copy of $\mathcal{L}$. Then as (1) holds and as $\|\phi(S_{\mu\nu})\| = \|S_{\mu\nu}\|$ because ϕ is an algebraic isomorphism, and $\|\sum_\mu S_{\mu\nu}(\eta(y))_\mu\|^2 = \|\sum_\mu \phi(S_{\mu\nu})y_\nu\|^2$, it follows that the condition corresponding to (1) holds in the case of the matrix $((\phi(S_{\mu\nu})))$, so that $((\phi(S_{\mu\nu})))$ is the matrix of an operator in $\mathcal{N}'$.

Now if $((S'_{\mu\nu}))$ is the matrix of an operator S' in $\mathcal{N}'$, to show that Φ is onto we need only show that $\sum_\nu \|\sum_\mu \phi^{-1}(S'_{\mu\nu})x_\mu\|^2$ is a convergent sum. If $x_{\mu\sigma}$ is as in the preceding paragraph, we observe that $(\phi^{-1}(S'_{\mu\nu})x_\mu)_\sigma = S'_{\mu\nu}x_{\mu\sigma}$, so $\|\sum_\mu \phi^{-1}(S'_{\mu\nu})x_\mu\|^2$
$= \|\sum_\mu \sum_\sigma S'_{\mu\nu}x_{\mu\sigma}\|^2 = \|\sum_\sigma \sum_\mu S'_{\mu\nu}x_{\mu\sigma}\|^2 =$
$\sum_\sigma \|\sum_\mu S'_{\mu\nu}x_{\mu\sigma}\|^2$. It follows that $\sum_\nu \|\sum_\mu \phi^{-1}(S'_{\mu\nu})x_\mu\|^2$
$= \sum_\nu \sum_\sigma \|\sum_\mu S'_{\mu\nu}x_{\mu\sigma}\|^2 = \sum_\sigma \sum_\nu \|\sum_\mu S'_{\mu\nu}x_{\mu\sigma}\|^2 \leq$
$\sum_\sigma \|S'\|^2 \sum_\mu \|x_{\mu\sigma}\|^2 = \|S\|^2 \sum_{\sigma,\mu} \|x_{\mu\sigma}\|^2 = \|S\|^2 \|x\|^2$.
To see that Φ is a homomorphism, observe that it is a homomorphism on the subalgebra of operators whose matrices have only a finite number of nonzero coordinates, because ϕ is a homomorphism, so that by the validity of the standard rules for matrix operations and the strong density of

that subalgebra (cf. [5] , p. 137) it is a homomorphism on the entire algebra.

Thus $\mathcal{H}'$ and $\mathcal{Q}'$ are algebraically isomorphic. Now $\mathcal{H}$ is of type I, as it is commutative, so every projection in $\mathcal{H}'$ is the L. U. B. of projections of type M. As L. U. B.s of projections and the concept of projection of type M are preserved under algebraic isomorphisms, it follows that every projection in $\mathcal{Q}'$ is the L. U. B. of projections of type M, - i. e., $\mathcal{Q}$ is of type I.

PROOF OF THEOREM. Let $\mathcal{Q}$ be a W*-algebra on $\mathcal{H}$ of type I. From Lemma 10.6 it follows readily that there exists a family $\{P_\mu\}$ of mutually orthogonal projections in the center of $\mathcal{Q}$ such that the contraction of $\mathcal{Q}$ to $P_\mu \mathcal{H}$ is unitarily equivalent to an $n(\mu)$-fold copy of a hyper-reducible algebra, and $\bigcup_\mu P_\mu$ is the maximal projection in $\mathcal{Q}$. The proof of Lemma 2.2 shows that if $\{Q_\nu\}$ are mutually orthogonal projections in the center of a W*-algebra $\mathcal{C}$ such that the contraction of $\mathcal{C}$ to $Q_\nu \mathcal{H}$ is hyper-reducible, then the contraction of $\mathcal{C}$ to $(\bigcup_\nu Q_\nu)\mathcal{H}$ is likewise hyper-reducible. Putting $Q_m = \bigcup_{n(\mu)=m} P_\mu$, it follows that the contraction of $\mathcal{Q}$ to $Q_m \mathcal{H}$ is unitarily equivalent to an m-fold copy of a hyper-reducible algebra, and clearly the Q_m are mutually orthogonal and $\bigcup_m Q_m$ is the maximal projection in $\mathcal{Q}$.

Conversely, let the W*-algebra $\mathcal{Q}$ on $\mathcal{H}$ be such that there exists a family $\{P_n\}$ of projections in the center of $\mathcal{Q}'$ and such that $I-P_0$ is the maximal projection in $\mathcal{Q}$, the contraction of $\mathcal{Q}$ to $P_n \mathcal{H}$ is unitarily equivalent to an n-fold copy of a hyper-reducible algebra. To show that $\mathcal{Q}$ is of type I it suffices to show that any such n-fold copy is of type I, and this is the statement of Lemma 10.8. Finally, the uniqueness part of the theorem follows without difficulty from Theorem 9.

COROLLARY 10.1. _If a W*-algebra is of type I, then so is its commutor._

It is easily seen that it suffices to prove the corollary for the case in which the algebra $\mathcal{Q}$ in question is an n-fold copy of a hyper-reducible algebra $\mathcal{D}$. To show that $\mathcal{Q}'$ is of type I is to show that every nonzero projection in $\mathcal{Q}$ contains a nonzero projection of type M. Now $\mathcal{D}'$ is commutative so, by Lemma 10.7, every nonzero projection in $\mathcal{D}$ contains a nonzero projection of type M, and as $\mathcal{D}$ and $\mathcal{Q}$ are algebraically isomorphic, it follows that the same is true of $\mathcal{Q}$.

COROLLARY 10.2. <u>A W*-algebra of type I is algebraically isomorphic to a hyper-reducible algebra via a mapping onto the hyper-reducible algebra that is weakly continuous and preserves the operational calculus for normal operators.</u>

The proof of this is a slight modification of part of the proof of Theorem 5.

The next result is essentially equivalent to the non-trivial part of Theorem IV of [5].

COROLLARY 10.3. (<u>Murray</u> <u>and</u> <u>von</u> <u>Neumann</u>). <u>A factor whose commutor contains a minimal projection is unitarily equivalent to an m-fold copy of the algebra of all operators on an n-dimensional Hilbert space, for unique cardinals m and n.</u>

Let $\mathcal{F}$ be a factor on $\mathcal{H}$ whose commutor contains a minimal projection E, and let P be an arbitrary nonzero projection in $\mathcal{F}'$. Then the L. U. B. of U*EU as U ranges over the unitary operators in $\mathcal{F}'$ is a projection in the center of $\mathcal{F}'$, and so equals I. It follows that the operator T = PU*EUP is nonzero for some U, as otherwise it is easily deduced that P = 0, but T is SA and non-negative so that it can be uniformly approximated by linear combinations of projections Q such that $\alpha Q \leq T$ for some $\alpha > 0$. Now $T \leq$ U*EU, from which it follows

that Q vanishes except on the range of U*EU, so Q $\leq$ U*EU; and as Ξ is
minimal, so also is U*EU, and it follows that Q = U*EU. It results
that T is a scalar multiple of U*EU and it is easy to see that T =
U*EU. Hence $\mathcal{F}$ is of type I in the sense of Definition 9.1.

As the center of $\mathcal{F}$ is trivial, it follows from the theorem
that it is unitarily equivalent to an m-fold copy of a hyper-reducible alge-
bra $\mathcal{D}$ on $\mathcal{K}$. Now $\mathcal{F}'$ contains the corresponding copy of $\mathcal{D}'$ on $\mathcal{K}$,
and $\mathcal{D}' \subset \mathcal{D}$, so $\mathcal{F} \cap \mathcal{F}'$ contains this latter m-fold copy. It
follows that $\mathcal{D}'$ consists only of scalars, so $\mathcal{D}$ is the algebra of all
operators on $\mathcal{K}$. That m and n are unique is clear from the uniqueness
part of the theorem.

Remark 9.2. In view of the special rôle in the foregoing of commutative W*-algebras of uniform multiplicity we should mention a relatively
concrete form for such. If $\mathcal{Q}$ on $\mathcal{H}$ is the n-fold copy of a masa algebra $\mathcal{M}$ on $\mathcal{K}$, then $\mathcal{M}$ can be taken as the multiplication algebra of a
measure space M = (R, $\mathcal{R}$, r) which is the direct sum of the finite per-
fect measure spaces $M_\lambda = (R_\lambda, \mathcal{R}_\lambda, r_\lambda)$; $\mathcal{H}$ can plainly be taken as
the collection of all indexed families $f_\mu(p)$ of functions on R with
μ ranging over an index set Ω of cardinality n, and such that $f_\mu(.)$
$\in$ L$_2$(M) for all μ and with the sum $\Sigma_\mu \| f_\mu \|^2$ convergent; and
$\mathcal{Q}$ is then the algebra of all operators A on $\mathcal{H}$ of the form $(Af)_\mu(p)$
$= k(p)f_\mu(p)$, where k is a bounded measurable function on M. Now let
$\mathcal{L}$ be a Hilbert space of dimension n. A function T(.) on M to the
(bounded) operators on $\mathcal{L}$ is called strongly measurable if, whenever m(.)
is a strongly measurable square-integrable function on M to $\mathcal{L}$ (i. e.
m is n. e. the limit of a sequence of simple functions, and $\| m(p) \|^2$ is
integrable on M), then the function n defined by the equation n(p) =
T(p)m(p) is again a measurable function on M to $\mathcal{L}$; and T(.) is called
bounded in case $\| T(p) \|$ is bounded as p ranges over R. Now regarding

$\mathcal{L}$ as the space of all complex-valued functions $f_\cdot$ on Ω such that the sum $\sum_\mu |f_\mu|^2$ is convergent and with $(f, g) = \sum_\mu f_\mu \bar{g}_\mu$ for any two such functions, there corresponds to any bounded strongly measurable function $T(.)$ on M a (unique) operator T on $\mathcal{H}$ such that for any f and g in $\mathcal{H}$, $(Tf, g) = \int_R (T(p)f_\cdot(p), g_\cdot(p))_L \, dr(p)$, where $(.., ..)_L$ indicates an inner product in $\mathcal{L}$; this follows readily from the observation that the integral exists and defines a continuous function of f and g which is linear in f and conjugate linear in g. We can now state:

<u>The</u> <u>operator</u> T <u>is in</u> Q', <u>and</u> <u>every</u> <u>element</u> <u>of</u> Q' <u>has this form</u>, <u>i. e.</u>, <u>for every</u> T <u>in</u> Q' <u>there is a bounded measurable function</u> T(.) <u>on</u> M <u>to</u> $\mathcal{L}$ <u>such that for any</u> f <u>in</u> $\mathcal{H}$, $(Tf)_\cdot(p) = T(p)(f_\cdot(p))$. <u>If</u> S <u>and</u> T <u>are elements of</u> Q' <u>to which correspond in this fashion the functions</u> S(.) <u>and</u> T(.), <u>and if</u> α <u>is a complex number</u>, <u>then the following equations are valid</u> n. e. <u>on</u> M: $(S+T)(p) = S(p) + T(p)$, $(ST)(p) = S(p)T(p)$, $(\alpha S)(p) = \alpha(S(p))$, <u>and</u> $S*(p) = (S(p))*$. A similar result is stated for the case when $\mathcal{L}$ and $\mathcal{K}$ are separable in $[2]$, q. v.

   The only point which offers any difficulty is the fact that every element of Q' has the stated form. Now as shown above there is a natural correspondence between Q' and appropriate n × n matrices over $\mathcal{M}$. Let the element T of Q' correspond to the matrix $((T_{\mu\nu}))$, where $\mu, \nu \in \Omega$ and $T_{\mu\nu}$ is the operation of multiplication by $k_{\mu\nu}$ on $L_2(M)$, where $k_{\mu\nu}$ can be taken to be bounded and continuous on each $\mathcal{M}_\lambda$. The boundedness of T means that $\sum_\nu \|\sum_\mu T_{\mu\nu} f_\mu\|^2 \leq \|T\|^2 \sum_\mu \|f_\mu\|^2$ for any $f \in \mathcal{H}$, or $\int (\sum_\nu |\sum_\mu k_{\mu\nu}(p)f_\mu(p)|^2) \, dr(p) \leq \|T\|^2 \int \sum_\mu |f_\mu(p)|^2 \, dr(p)$. As this equation remains valid when each f_μ is multiplied by the characteristic function of a measurable set, it results that n. e. on M, $\sum_\nu |\sum_\mu k_{\mu\nu}(p)f_\mu(p)|^2 \leq \|T\|^2 \sum_\mu |f_\mu(p)|^2$. In particular, if f_μ vanishes except for a finite set F of μ's, and if for each μ, f_μ is continuous on each R_λ, and if G is any finite set of indices we have

$$\sum_{\nu \in G} \left| \sum_{\mu \in F} k_{\mu\nu}(p) f_\mu(p) \right|^2 \leq \|T\|^2 \sum_{\mu \in F} |f_\mu(p)|^2, \text{ n. e.}$$

As both sides of this inequality are continuous on each R_λ, and as the complement of a null set in a finite perfect measure is dense in the space, the inequality is valid for every $p \in R$, and since G is an arbitrary finite set of indices we can conclude that

$$\sum_\nu \left| \sum_{\mu \in F} k_{\mu\nu}(p) f_\mu(p) \right|^2 \leq \|T\|^2 \sum_{\mu \in F} |f_\mu(p)|^2 \quad \text{for all}$$

$p \in R$. Hence there exists a (bounded) operator $T(p)$ on $\mathcal{L}$ with matrix $((k_{\mu\nu}(p)))$ (relative to the obvious basis), with $\|T(p)\| \leq \|T\|$, and such that $T(p)f_.(p) = (Tf)_.(p)$, for f as above. It is readily seen that for any $f \in \mathcal{H}$ there is a sequence $\{f^1\}$ in $\mathcal{H}$, each f^1 being as above, - so that $T(p)f^1_.(p) = (Tf^1)_.(p)$, - and such that f^1 converges to f in $\mathcal{H}$; for nearly all p, $f^1_.(p) \longrightarrow f_.(p)$ in $\mathcal{L}$, and with $(Tf^1)_.(p) \longrightarrow (Tf)_.(p)$ in $\mathcal{L}$ for nearly all p. It follows that for all f in $\mathcal{H}$, $(Tf)_.(p) = T(p)f_.(p)$ n. e. on M, and $T(.)$ is a bounded strongly measurable function on $\mathcal{M}$ to the operators on $\mathcal{L}$.

REFERENCES

1.   I. Kaplansky, Projections in Banach algebras. Ann. Math. 53(1951) 235-249.

2.   G. W. Mackey, A theorem of Stone and von Neumann. Duke Math. Jour. 16(1949) 313-326.

3.   D. Maharam, On homogeneous measure algebras. Proc. Nat. Acad. Sci. 28(1942) 108-111.

4.   N. H. McCoy, Rings and ideals. Baltimore, 1948.

5.   F. J. Murray and J. von Neumann, On rings of operators. Ann. Math. 37(1936) 116-229.

6.   H. Nakano, Unitärinvarianten hypermaximale normale Operatoren. Ann. Math. 42(1941) 657-664.

7.   _________, Unitärinvarianten im allgemeinen euklidischer Raum. Math. Ann. 118(1941/43) 112-133.

8.   A. I. Plessner and V. A. Rokhlin, Spectral theory of linear operators. II (in Russian). Uspekhi. Mat. Nauk (N.S.) 1(1946) 71-191. Cf. Math. Rev. 9(1948), p. 43.

9.   I. E. Segal, Decompositions of operator algebras. I. Submitted to Memoirs Amer. Math. Soc.

10.   _________, Equivalences of measure spaces.   Amer. Jour. Math. 73(1951) 275-313.

11.   _________, Postulates for general quantum mechanics. Ann. Math. 48(1947) 930-948.

12.   _________, A class of operator algebras which are determined by groups. Duke Math. Jour. 18(1951) 221-265.

13. J. von Neumann, Über Funktionen von Funktionaloperatoren. Ann. Math. 32(1931) 191-226.

14. F. Wecken, Unitärinvarianten selbstadjunjierter Operatoren. Math. Ann. 116(1939) 422-455.